Experimental

NUCLEAR CHEMISTRY

GREGORY R. CHOPPIN
The Florida State University

PRENTICE-HALL, INC.
Englewood Cliffs, N. J.
1961

PRENTICE-HALL CHEMISTRY SERIES

Kenneth S. Pitzer, editor

Experimental

NUCLEAR CHEMISTRY

Preface

Many new experimental tools have been placed in the hands of the physical scientists in the last fifteen years. These have been used to probe more widely and more deeply into the nature of matter. Of all the new techniques, none have been employed in more diverse means nor yielded greater rewards to the user than radioactive isotopes. In medicine, agriculture, industry, and research, radioactivity has answered many scientific and technological questions to the benefit of mankind. It has been estimated that, in the United States alone, industry is saving close to a billion dollars annually through the use of radioactivity. Thus, it has not been necessary to wait for the development of economic nuclear power from reactors to realize great benefits from the atom.

Although the use of radioactive isotopes increased at a very rapid rate after 1946 when the United States Atomic Energy Commission began making them available, the A. E. C. in an attempt to further accelerate this rate announced in 1958 a new program of support for research into technical applications of isotopes. Under this and similar programs, universities and colleges were urged to institute or to expand laboratory courses designed to teach students to use this new tool effectively and safely. With such an increasingly widespread utilization of radioactivity into all aspects of American technology, it may be almost a necessity for a scientist to be knowledgeable concerning the techniques of nuclear and radiochemistry. The non-nuclear chemist is often reluctant to use radioisotopes in his research, because of the idea that their use involves extensive revision of techniques, and extreme care in handling. There are special problems involved, but it is hoped that a discussion of their nature will help to reduce them. Some familiarity with the great advantages of radioisotope use, coupled with intelligent awareness of their unique safety requirements, can only promote a much more extensive employment of radioisotopes in all areas of science. For the student who is contemplating, or who has already decided to work in the area of nuclear science or the atomic energy industry, a thorough knowledge of the physical and chemical techniques involved in this field is essential. It is the author's hope that this book will encourage the use of radioactive isotopes in scientific research.

Chapters III–VII cover the basic knowledge needed to detect and measure radioactivity accurately. These experiments are suggested for all students, no matter what their particular field of chemical interest. In Chapters VIII–XII the intent has been to present a diversity of experiments so as to allow the instructor to assign some experiments to conform with the field of interest of the individual students. Unless otherwise noted, the experiments can be completed in a three-hour laboratory session. This depends on student advance preparation, and availability of necessary materials. It is best to give each student his semester assignment in the first few sessions so that he may prepare solutions, and the like, ahead of time. It has been found very helpful to have a one-hour lecture meeting a week to discuss the theory behind the experiments.

No experiments have been included in which biochemical studies of living systems are illustrated. It has seemed better to urge biochemical students to perform more experiments of a physical, chemical, and analytical nature, and then to do a short special project (Appendix A) of their own choosing.

Since nuclear chemistry is a young branch of the science of chemistry, and one closely allied with nuclear physics, the basic library sources of information in this area are not always the traditional ones for chemists. *Chemical Abstracts* and *Analytical Chemistry*, in particular, are very useful, the latter increasingly so for radiochemical separations and activation analysis. However, there are a number of other journals which carry much nuclear data, among which are *The Journal of Inorganic and Nuclear Chemistry*, *Physical Review*, and *Physical Review Letters*. *Nuclear Science Abstracts*, published monthly by the U.S. Government Printing Office, includes abstracts of laboratory reports, as well as abstracts of published papers.

For more complete data on the nuclear properties of the isotopes listed in Appendix B, and for data on the other known isotopes, the compilations by the Nuclear Data Group of the National Academy of Sciences–National Research Council, published quarterly in the Nuclear Science Abstracts are very useful. The data published by Strominger, Hollander, and Seaborg [*Revs. Modern Phys.*, *30*, 585 (1958)] is also very helpful. A great deal of this information on half lives, decay modes, and energies of the radiations are included on a *Chart of the Nuclides* available upon request from the General Electric Company, Schenectady, New York (Department 2-119). W. H. Sullivan has included the same type of information in *Trilinear Chart of the Nuclides* available for $2.00 from the Government Printing Office.

Review articles on all phases of nuclear science are to be found in the journal *Review of Modern Physics* and in collections such as *Annual Reviews of Nuclear Science* (Stanford), and *Progress in Nuclear Physics* (Academic Press). For a comprehensive guide to review articles, separation procedures, and nuclear data summaries, *A Directory to Nuclear Data Tabulations* (Government Printing Office, Washington 25, D. C., $0.70),

and *Source Material for Radiochemistry* (Nuclear Science Series, Report No. 27, National Academy of Science, Washington) are recommended strongly. Of course, many other sources of excellent reference articles have not been mentioned in this brief discussion. The serious student of nuclear science must be familiar with the British, Canadian, French, German, and Russian literature, as well as the American.

Experience has shown that it is helpful to have at hand throughout the course a text dealing with the basic aspects of nuclear science. Brief introductory summaries to the pertinent theoretical aspects underlying the experiments described are included in this book, but the enterprising and curious student will desire fuller explanations beyond the scope of this book. Others which can serve are: *Nuclear and Radiochemistry*, G. Friedlander and J. Kennedy, John Wiley and Sons (1955); *The Atomic Nucleus*, R. E. Evans, McGraw-Hill Book Company, Inc. (1955); *Introductory Nuclear Physics*, D. Halliday, John Wiley and Sons (1955); *Nuclear Radiation Physics*, R. E. Lapp and H. L. Andrews, Prentice-Hall, Inc. (1956); *Sourcebook on Atomic Energy*, S. Glasstone, D. Van Nostrand Co. (1950).

It is a pleasure to acknowledge the assistance given by many professional colleagues in the way of discussions and suggestions. A. Caretto, R. Carr, R. Johnsen, R. Johnson, C. Mann, W. W. Meinke, H. Plendl, and A. Voight have helped by generously providing copies of experiments, and giving advice. The students of the course at Florida State University have served as willing guinea pigs to debug these experiments, and in this way are true co-authors. To Dr. B. G. Harvey is owed a considerable debt of gratitude for suggesting this book and assisting with valuable suggestions and criticisms in its preparation. Finally, I would like to thank my wife, Ann, for her sympathetic understanding and encouragement in this endeavor.

Contents

Experiments

1. Use of radiation detection instruments
2. Geiger-Müller counters
3. Proportional counters
4. Sample preparation
5. Counting statistics
6. Scattering
7. Sample self-absorption
8. Absorption curves and range-energy of beta particles
9. Gamma absorption curves
10. Half life determination
11. Radioactive equilibrium (I)
12. Radioactive equilibrium (II)
13. Scintillation counting
14. Beta spectrum analysis
15. Gamma spectrometry
16. Neutron flux determination
17. Neutron activation of silver
18. Szilard-Chalmers reaction (I)
19. Szilard-Chalmers reaction (II)
20. Szilard-Chalmers reaction (III)
21. Isotopic precipitation
22. Coprecipitation
23. Electrodeposition of cobalt
24. Electrodeposition of uranium
25. Separation of alkali metal ions
26. Separation of Ce and Pr by ion exchange
27. Anion exchange resin separation
28. Solvent extraction
29. Paper chromatography (I)
30. Paper chromatography (II)
31. Isotopic exchange reaction
32. Structure of nickel cyanide
33. Determination of ionic charge

I

Nuclear Stability

THE existence of radioisotopes is evidence that not all atomic nuclei are stable. Some of the unstable nuclei decay by alpha particle emission, others by beta particle emission, and still others by capture of orbital electrons. Gamma-ray emission may also accompany these changes. Intelligent application of radioisotopes in scientific research requires some understanding of the theoretical basis for nuclear instability. This theory allows us to understand the reason for the type of decay and the energy changes involved for any particular unstable nuclide. In turn, understanding of the type of decay and the energy involved provides answers to practical questions concerning the type of counting system to use and the type of counting sample to prepare. The tremendous range in the rates of radioactive decay, from shorter than 10^{-9} second to longer than 10^9 years, is understandable from the theory of nuclear instability.

Since nuclei contain protons, it is obvious that a repulsive coulombic force will exist between these positive particles within the nucleus itself. The existence of nuclei means, therefore, that there must also be another force present which is strong enough to counterbalance the protonic repulsion and hold the nucleons together. While the nature of this nuclear force is not clearly understood at present, many types of experiments have provided information about its properties, of which two are of interest here. First of all, it has a very short range—essentially existing only between a nucleon and its immediate neighbors (approximately 10^{-13} cm). The coulombic force, on the other hand, has a long range so that the influence of each proton present is felt over the whole nucleus. The second property of the nuclear force is that it is charge independent. The nuclear force of attraction between two neutrons is equal to that between two protons or between a neutron and a proton. Of course, the coulombic force exists only between protons.

Neutron to Proton Ratio

For elements at the beginning of the periodic table, it is found that saturation of nuclear forces resulting in stable nuclides is best achieved by

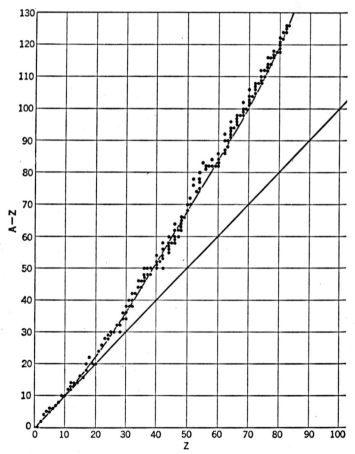

Figure 1. Plot of the number of neutrons $(A-Z)$ vs. the number of protons Z for stable nuclei ($> 10\%$ abundance).

having equal numbers of protons and neutrons. Helium-4, carbon-12, oxygen-16, and neon-20 are only a few examples of this situation. As Z increases, so does the repulsive coulombic force but at a more rapid rate than the stabilizing nuclear force. This is a consequence of the long range nature of the former. The coulombic force follows the normal inverse square law. To decrease this disruptive force, it is necessary to move the protons farther apart by the addition of extra neutrons. As a result, the neutron to proton (n/p) ratio of the stable nuclides, which has a value of unity in the first atomic period, begins to increase. This n/p ratio for stable nuclides finally reaches a value of 1.5 at Bi^{209}. Above bismuth, the nuclides also become unstable to alpha decay. The value of n/p necessary for stability for any element is not unique but rather there is usually a small range of values over which stable nuclides can exist. This is particularly true for elements of even Z which in general have several stable isotopes. Elements of odd Z usually have only 1 or 2 stable isotopes. For example, element 50 (tin) has stable isotopes ranging from $A = 112$ to $A = 124$. The stable n/p range in tin is from 1.24 to 1.48. For indium and antimony, the odd Z elements on either side, the ranges are only 1.31 to 1.35 and 1.37 to 1.41, respectively. (See Figure 1.)

If a nucleus has a high n/p ratio, it is said to be neutron rich. It will be unstable and will decay in a manner that will tend to bring the n/p ratio closer to the stable value. In this case, it must lower N and increase Z which can be done by conversion of a neutron to a proton within the nucleus. When this occurs, a negative electron is emitted as a beta (β^-) particle, e.g.,

$$_{49}In^{116} \longrightarrow {}_{50}Sn^{116} + \beta^-$$

If the n/p ratio is too low, then the decay will be such as to lower Z and increase N by conversion of a proton to a neutron. This may be accomplished by emission of a positron (β^+ decay) or by absorption by the nucleus of an orbital electron (electron capture). Two such reactions are

$$_{51}Sb^{116} \longrightarrow {}_{50}Sn^{116} + \beta^+$$

and

$$_{79}Au^{195} \xrightarrow{\text{E.C.}} {}_{78}Pt^{195}$$

β^+ decay and electron capture are competing processes with the probability of the latter increasing as Z increases. In the early part of the periodic chart, unstable neutron-deficient nuclides decay by positron emission. For the elements in the platinum region and beyond, decay occurs predominantly by electron capture. Both processes are seen in isotopes of the elements in the middle portion of the periodic chart.

The formation of a more stable nucleus as a result of radioactive decay is accompanied by a release of energy. This energy, which is called the decay energy Q, usually appears mainly as kinetic energy of the emitted particle and of any neutrinos ejected, but also partly as gamma radiation in many cases. Much valuable quantitative information on the stability of nuclei may be gained by the application of the Principle of Conservation of Energy to nuclear decay processes. In nuclear transformations the magnitude of the energy changes are so great that they can be calculated from the difference in masses of the reactant system and the product system. Of course, this is theoretically possible in thermochemistry, but the mass differences in those systems are several orders of magnitude less than the accuracy with which the masses are known. Nuclear transformations are on the order of 10^5 to 10^6 more energetic than chemical reactions on an individual molecular or atomic basis. From the relationship $E = mc^2$, it is possible to calculate that one atomic mass unit is equivalent to 931 Mev. Since nuclear transformation energies run from the kev to the Mev range, mass differences of a millimass unit are common. This will represent almost $5 \times 10^{-4}\%$ of the total mass even in the heaviest elements, which is an easily measurable amount.

If the masses are known, it is a simple matter to calculate the decay energy in radioactive decay. Consider the reaction mentioned above

$$_{49}\mathrm{In}^{116} \longrightarrow {}_{50}\mathrm{Sn}^{116} + \beta^- + Q$$

If Q represents the decay energy and M the atomic masses,

$$Q = 931[(M_{\mathrm{In}}^{116}) - (M_{\mathrm{Sn}}^{116})] = 931[115.94096 - 115.93779]$$
$$= 931[0.00317] = 2.95 \text{ Mev}$$

The 931 is necessary to convert mass units to Mev according to the mass-energy relationship given earlier.

This type of calculation may be used in a wider application to consider the energy change involved when a nucleus is formed from its constituent nucleons. Consider helium-4. The formation is represented by

$$2n + 2p^+ \longrightarrow \mathrm{He}^4 + Q$$
$$Q = 931[2M_n + 2M_p - M_{\mathrm{He}}^4]$$
$$= 931[(2 \times 1.00893 + 2 \times 1.00812) - 4.00390]$$
$$= 931[4.03410 - 4.00390] = 931[0.03020]$$
$$= 28.12 \text{ Mev}$$

The fact that it is highly improbable that He^4 would ever be made by such a four-body collision does not invalidate the calculation. As in ordinary thermodynamics, only the initial and final states are important and not the particular path followed. This 28.12 Mev of energy is known as the *binding energy* of the He^4 nucleus as it is the exact amount of energy necessary to break this nucleus into its individual nucleons and hence is a measure of its stability. Related to the binding energy (B.E.) is the value B.E./A or average binding energy per nucleon which is about 7 Mev for the He^4 nucleus. This is another mode of expression of relative nuclear

stability. In Figure 2 this quantity B.E./A is plotted as a function of A. The maxima at certain values (e.g., 4, 12, etc.) reflect unusual stability for these values of A. Calculations of this type may be used to demonstrate that above bismuth, emission of alpha particles is exoergic. This accounts for alpha activity in the heavy elements.

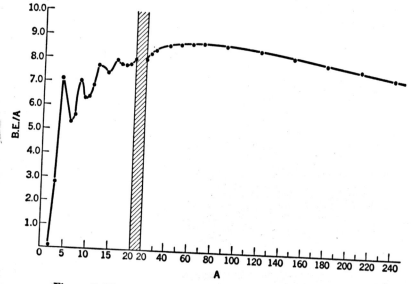

Figure 2. Plot of the binding energy per nucleon (Mev/nucleon) as a function of the mass number.

If two different nuclides have the same values of A, it is very improbable that their binding energies will be exactly equal. Therefore, it is a premise of nuclear stability rules that adjacent isobars (nuclides of same A but different Z) cannot both be stable. An example of this was given earlier in the decay of In^{116} to Sn^{116}. Here, as in all cases, the heavier nucleus (lower binding energy) will decay to the lighter one; that is, the reaction will be exoergic. We have now expressed via nuclear thermodynamics a more quantitative concept of nuclear stability than the n/p ratio provided. The concept that the larger the binding energy ("heat of formation") the more stable the nucleus, is one which chemists should readily appreciate.

The binding energy for the addition of a nucleon is used frequently. For the addition of a neutron to He^3, the energy liberated is 20.5 Mev, while for the addition of a neutron to He^4 it is -0.8 Mev. The difference in the value of the binding energy of the additional neutron in He^3 and He^4 clearly shows the relative stability of the two nuclei, He^4 and He^5. In addition, the -0.8 Mev value for He^5 indicates that the system $He^4 + n$ is at a lower energy level than He^5. As a consequence, He^5 is a very unstable nuclide.

All masses used here and in similar calculations are atomic masses and not nuclear masses. This practice avoids the necessity in most cases of adding and subtracting electron masses in these equations. Without any further discussion, it is possible to present three rules to be followed when atomic masses are used:

(1) In equations involving negatron (β^-), electron capture, or alpha decay, it is not necessary to add or subtract electron masses.

(2) In equations involving positron (β^+) emission, it is necessary to add an additional two electron masses (i.e., 1.02 Mev) to the difference in masses of initial and product nuclei in order to obtain Q.

(3) It is not necessary to add electron masses in equations of nuclear reactions induced by charged particles or neutrons.

PROBLEMS

1. Predict the most probable mode of decay and calculate the decay energy for

	Masses:	
(a) $_{27}Co^{58}$	$_{26}Fe^{58}$	57.9515
	$_{27}Co^{58}$	57.9536
	$_{28}Ni^{60}$	57.9536
(b) $_{15}P^{32}$	$_{14}Si^{32}$	31.9841
	$_{15}P^{32}$	31.9840
	$_{16}S^{32}$	31.9821
(c) $_{58}Ce^{141}$	$_{57}La^{141}$	140.9543
	$_{58}Ce^{141}$	140.9517
	$_{59}Pr^{141}$	140.9511

2. Calculate the total binding energy and the binding energy per nucleon for:

	Masses:	
(a) $_{12}Mg^{24}$	$_{12}Mg^{24}$	23.9926
(b) $_{27}Co^{60}$	$_{27}Co^{60}$	59.9523
(c) $_{79}Au^{197}$	$_{79}Au^{197}$	197.0391

3. Show that $_{94}Pu^{241}$ is unstable to both alpha and beta emission.

	Masses:	
	$_{94}Pu^{241}$	241.1256
	$_{95}Am^{241}$	241.1314
	$_{92}U^{237}$	237.1220

4. $_{39}Y^{90}$ decays by β^- emission to $_{40}Zr^{90}$. If the decay energy, Q_β, is measured to be 2.26 Mev and the mass of Zr^{90} is determined by mass spectrometry to be 89.9329, what is the mass of Y^{90}?

5. In natural indium, In^{115} is found in 95.8% abundance; in natural tin, Sn^{115} is found in 0.38% abundance. Which would be expected to be unstable with respect to the other, and what approximate lower limit can be given the half life

since this nuclide is still found in nature if the age of the elements is assumed to be 7×10^9 years? Calculate the mode and energy of decay.

Masses:
$$\text{In}^{115} = 114.9391$$
$$\text{Sn}^{115} = 114.9385$$

6. The mass of $_{10}\text{Ne}^{22}$ is 21.9984. The mass of $_{11}\text{Na}^{22}$ is 22.0014. What is the Q for the reaction

$$_{11}\text{Na}^{22} \longrightarrow {_{10}\text{Ne}^{22}} + \beta^+ + Q?$$

7. Assume that U^{235} fissions when struck by a neutron. If $_{42}\text{Mo}^{95}$, $_{57}\text{La}^{139}$, and 2 neutrons are the final products, calculate the energy released in the fission process and the subsequent beta decay if the initial neutron is assumed to have zero kinetic energy.

Masses:
$$\text{U}^{235} = 235.116$$
$$\text{Mo}^{95} = 94.045$$
$$\text{La}^{139} = 138.955$$

8. The fusion reaction

$$_1\text{H}^2 + {_1\text{H}^3} \longrightarrow {_2\text{He}^4} + n$$

liberates 17.6 Mev of energy. If the mass of deuterium is measured to be 2.0147 in a mass spectrometer, what is the mass of the isotope of hydrogen with $A = 3$ (tritium)?

REFERENCES

Cameron, A. G. W., "Nuclear Masses," *Can. J. Phys.*, **35**, 1021 (1957).

Evans, R. D., *The Atomic Nucleus*. New York: McGraw-Hill Book Co., Inc., 1955, Chapter 3.

Friedlander, G., and J. Kennedy, *Nuclear and Radiochemistry*. New York: John Wiley & Sons, Inc., 1955, Chapter 2.

Glasstone, S., *Sourcebook on Atomic Energy*. New York: D. Van Nostrand Co., 1950, Chapter 12.

Halliday, D., *Introductory Nuclear Physics*. New York: John Wiley & Sons, Inc., 1955, Chapter 11.

Lapp, R. E., and H. L. Andrews, *Nuclear Radiation Physics*. Englewood Cliffs, N. J.: Prentice-Hall, Inc., 1954, Chapter 3.

II

Radiation Safety

WITH the public interest in the problem of radioactive fall-out so great, it is almost impossible for anyone to be unaware that radiation presents a danger. However, our daily life is full of dangerous situations which are accepted as the more or less normal hazards of present-day civilization. We could eliminate almost completely the tremendous toll which the automobile exacts by making the maximum speed 20 miles per hour. This is not done because the benefits obtained by higher speeds are in general considered to outweigh the hazards. Hydrogen sulfide is very poisonous and hydrofluoric acid quite dangerous to handle, yet they are in common use even in undergraduate chemical laboratories. The problem is identical for radioactive substances; the fact that they present a certain amount of danger is accepted because of the great benefits gained from their use. The same type of intelligent precautions that are used in handling chemicals such as H_2S and HF make radioisotope usage just as safe. In fact, since extremely small amounts of activity are easily detected by monitors and survey instruments, it is little trouble to keep track of the cleanliness of the working area and of the level of radiation encountered. When proper precautions and procedures are a partner to all radiochemical oper-

ations, then the experimenter is safer than in an ordinary chemical laboratory.

Biological Effects of Radiation

The energy of radiations from active nuclei is dissipated during passage through matter by ionization or excitation of atoms or molecules of the stopping material. In a biological system this ionization can cause damage directly by disruption of chemical bonds in the cell. Additionally, the radiation will interact with the water both inside and outside the cell to produce free radicals. These latter will damage the cell by causing oxidation-reduction reactions to occur. Even though the different types of radiation differ in the extent to which they will produce these effects, an important fact to keep in mind is that they will all produce the same effects. This means that the study of radiation effects induced by X rays can be extrapolated to predict those of alpha particles. The actual extent of the biological damage depends on many factors in addition to the type of radiation—for example, the energy of the radiation, the rate of administration of the radiation, the organ of the body irradiated, the age and the state of health of the individual. This makes it impossible to state that a certain definite number of disintegrations of any nuclide will produce a definite amount of some biological effect. However, in all cases, the amount of radiation energy necessary to produce observable biological effects is small. The quantity sufficient to cause death will result in a rise of only 0.001°C in the body temperature. This temperature rise is the result of conversion of radiation to thermal energy and is a symptom, not a cause, of the radiation injury. In view of this, radiation must always be considered damaging. Occasionally, following a small amount of irradiation, some stimulating effects are observed, but these are secondary effects which are the result of injury or destruction of some inhibitory agent by the radiation.

It seems quite certain that the blood-forming organs (spleen, bone marrow, etc.) are particularly susceptible to radiation damage and if these are protected there is an appreciable decrease in the over-all effect on the body. Likewise, immature, growing cells are more susceptible than adult cells and for this reason, people below 18 years of age should be guarded against all unnecessary exposure to radiation. The body does have the ability to recover from radiation effects, but there seem to be residual effects which may not be evident for a considerable length of time. Carcinogenesis and genetic mutations are two such possible long term effects but quantitative estimates of their probability as a function of the amount of irradiation is a subject of much study and debate at present. A third long term effect—acceleration of the aging process—has been estimated in a semi-quantitative way but it is not very large. If a person received the maximum permissible amount of radiation constantly for a twenty-year period—an extremely unlikely situation—the predicted life shortening would be a year.

Units of Radiation

Since radiation produces ionization in its passage through matter, thereby losing energy, the extent of the ionization has been used as a measure of the radiation field. However, it is necessary to introduce units which express the absorbed dose and not just the exposure dose.

The roentgen is defined as that quantity of γ- or X-ray irradiation which produces 1.16×10^{12} ion pairs in 1 gram of air. This is equivalent to the absorption of 87 ergs per gram of air. By definition the roentgen unit is limited to electromagnetic radiations (γ or X) and expresses the intensity of the radiation field, not the dose absorbed by an individual in that field.

The rad is the dose of any nuclear radiation which results in the absorption of 100 ergs per gram (of any material). This unit does express a measure of the absorbed dose and is not limited to any particular type of radiation.

The RBE (relative biological effectiveness) is defined as the ratio of the absorbed dose in rads of gamma radiation to the absorbed dose of the given radiation which is required to give the same biological effect. The necessity for this unit arises from the fact that the various types of radiations will be different in the effect which a specified dose has on the absorbing medium.

The rem (roentgen equivalent man) expresses the amount of radiation which produces the same biological effect as one rad; i.e., the dose in rems = RBE $\times$ dose in rads.

To calculate the dose in rems it is necessary to know the RBE. This is difficult, as the exact value depends on the type of radiation and its energy, the organ irradiated and the type of biological damage observed. Some typical values are presented in Table I. For a field of mixed radiations, the total dose in rems is equal to the sum of the product of the absorbed dose of each radiation and its RBE. Since roentgens are the units in which the monitor instruments are calibrated to read, and the difference between this unit and the rad is small, the dose in rems is frequently calculated using roentgens.

TABLE I

Radiation	RBE
X or γ ray	1
β ray	1
Alphas	20
Slow neutrons	5
Fast neutrons and protons (up to 10 Mev)	10

For gamma-ray emitters, an approximate relationship between radiation field and disintegration rate of a point source is expressed by Equation (II-1).

$$R/\text{hr at 1 foot} = 6 \times C \times E \times n \qquad \text{(II-1)}$$

where R = number of roentgens,

C = number of curies,

E = gamma energy in Mev,

n = number of quanta per disintegration.

This equation is most nearly valid for nuclides for which n has a value of unity and for energies between 0.07 and 3 Mev.

Maximum Permissible Exposure Level

Cosmic rays, dental and medical X rays, natural radioactivity in the earth which is retained in many construction materials, and now radioactive fall-out constitute a background amount of radiation to which everyone is subjected throughout his life. Somewhere between this inescapable amount and that known to cause serious injury, it is necessary to set an acceptable level for workers with radioactivity. At present this level, below which no permanent physiological changes have been observed to occur in the average individual, seems to be about 0.1 roentgen per day, but the period of observation is too short to be certain. In fact, it is impossible at present to be certain that any level is absolutely safe; therefore, it is necessary to establish levels which involve a risk comparable to or smaller than that encountered in other occupations. Since it is not possible to predict how long an individual might work with radioactivity, the permissible levels are based on the assumption that exposure will continue throughout his working life. Because of the uncertainties in the assessment of these levels, it is strongly recommended by all authorities on the subject that exposure be kept to a minimum.

The maximum permissible level recommended by the International Atomic Energy Agency is 0.1 rem per week. The U. S. Atomic Energy Commission accepts this limit for purposes of planning and design. The total amount of radiation accumulated at any age should not exceed the value obtained by use of Equation (II-2).

$$D = 5(N - 18) \qquad \text{(II-2)}$$

where D = dose in rems,

N = age in years.

To the extent permitted by this formula, an occupationally exposed person may accumulate the maximum permissible dose of radiation at a rate not in excess of 3 rems during any single 13 week period.

Although it is a relatively simple problem to measure the radiation which is received from an external source, it is very difficult to measure radiations from sources inside the body. These activities may enter in several ways and, depending on their chemical state and their biological chemistry, may constitute a considerable hazard. Some of the commonly used nuclides are listed in Table II according to their relative radiotoxicities.

TABLE II

I. Very High: Sr^{90}, Ra, Pu.

II. High: Ca^{45}, Fe^{55}, Y^{91}, Zr^{95}, Ce^{144}, Pm^{147}, Bi^{210}, Po.

III. Medium: H^3, C^{14}, Na^{22}, P^{32}, S^{35}, Cl^{36}, Mn^{54}, Fe^{59}, Co^{60} Sr^{89}, Nb^{95}, Ru^{103}, Ru^{106}, Te^{127}, Te^{129}, I^{131}, Cs^{137}, Ba^{140}, La^{140}, Ce^{141}, Pr^{143}, Nd^{147}, Au^{198}, Au^{199}, Hg^{203}, Hg^{205}.

IV. Low: Na^{24}, K^{42}, Cu^{64}, Mn^{52}, As^{76}, As^{77}, Kr^{85}, Hg^{197}.

The alpha particle emitters represent little hazard externally as these massive emissions are stopped by the outer layer of skin. Internally, however, heavy elements such as plutonium are concentrated in the most sensitive areas of the bone. There the alpha particles will provide essentially lifetime irradiation as the rate of atomic exchange is quite small. The large amount of energy is dissipated in a very localized area, considerably increasing the biological damage. Beta-ray emitters represent slightly more of an external hazard as their radiations are sufficiently penetrating to produce damage of the skin. Internally, their energy dissipation is over a somewhat larger volume than that for alpha emissions but still localized sufficiently to be very damaging to the tissue with which they are in contact. Elements such as Na, C, and S represent slight hazards as their

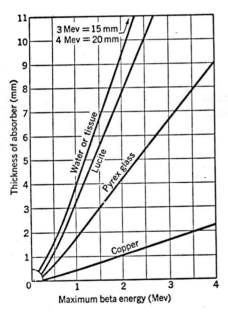

Figure 1. Thickness required for various materials to stop beta rays completely.

body chemistry does not tend to localize them in any particular organ and their exchange rate is high, leading to rapid elimination. Sr and I on the other hand are localized and retained. Gamma and X rays have

high penetrating power and constitute as much of an external hazard as an internal one.

Radiation Protection

Three basic principles are recommended for keeping radiation exposure to a minimum: shielding, control, and distance.

Since matter stops radiation, proper shields should provide considerable protection. For alpha emitters, even a thick piece of paper is sufficient to stop all the particles completely. The main hazard is absorption internally and not external irradiation. For solutions of nuclides which emit only beta particles, the glass walls of the container usually provide sufficient shielding. Sheets of glass or plastic (such as lucite) are used commonly to shield exposed solid samples (Figure 1). Because of the high penetrating power of γ and X rays, thick layers of concrete, water, steel, or lead must

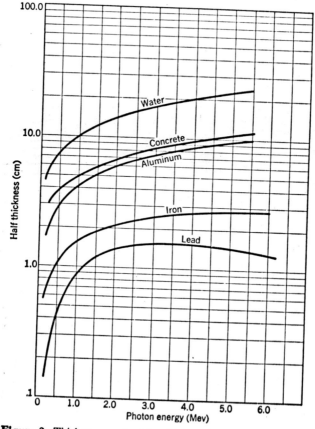

Figure 2. Thickness required for shielding to reduce photon intensity by 50%, as a function of photon energy.

be used (Figure 2). Neutrons are not discussed here as they are likely to be a hazard only in the immediate area of a reactor or accelerator.

Since the intensity falls off as the inverse square of the distance, isolation of unused isotopes and maintenance of maximum distance (by use, when necessary, of remote control apparatus such as the tongs shown in Figure 3) in working with moderate levels of activity reduce the exposure appreciably.

To reduce the possibility of internal absorption, and to minimize the chances of ruining experiments through accidental contamination, control

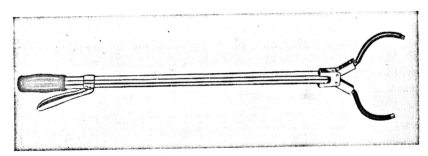

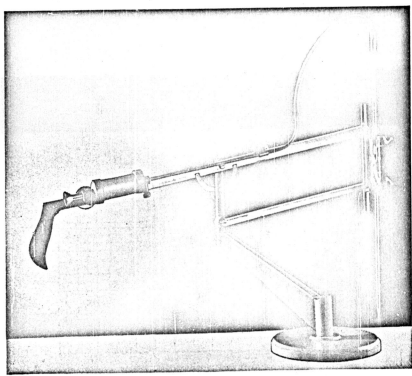

Figure 3. Remote control apparatus: tongs and pipetting equipment. (*Courtesy Nuclear-Chicago Corp.*)

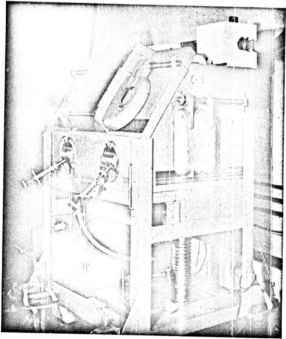

Figure 4. Upper photo shows a wooden glove box used for confining radioactivity. The two front ports are normally equipped with long rubber gloves. Bottom photo shows a small lead-shielded cave used for remote control operations involving higher levels of radioactivity. (*Photos courtesy Lawrence Radiation Laboratory*)

of the radioactivity to the minimum area necessary is essential. The ideal is absolutely no radioactivity except in the immediate working area and, even here, upon completion of the particular experiment, all activity should be removed and the area thoroughly decontaminated if necessary. For low levels, this means working in a good hood with easily cleaned non-porous surfaces such as stainless steel or painted wood. All bench tops should be non-porous also; formica has been used for this. For moderate levels, a glove box, such as the one shown in Figure 4, under slightly re-

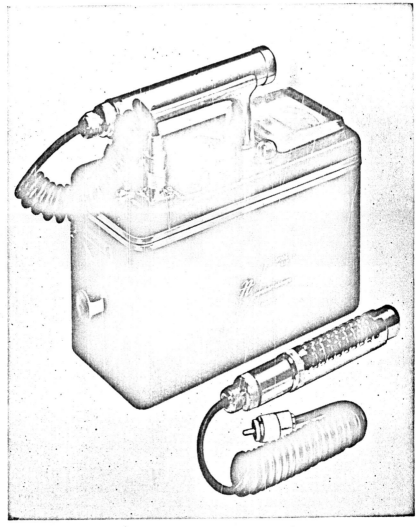

Figure 5. Portable survey meter. (*Courtesy Nuclear-Chicago Corp.*)

duced pressure provides a simple and convenient closed chemical laboratory. Such a box of simple design can be constructed for a modest sum from ordinary supplies and is an excellent means of confinement and containment of radioactivity. Of course, it does not provide shielding from gamma rays, but if these have sufficient intensity to make shielding necessary, a modified glove box can be inserted in a lead shell. Operations must be carried out by remote control in this case.

If a radiochemical laboratory is designed in such a fashion and the work performed in such a manner that the general background contamination is sufficiently low enough to do valid low-level tracer experiments, then, the health aspects of radiation control will be quite satisfactory. The regulations suggested at the end of this chapter are designed to help ensure this, and adherence to them is strongly recommended in all instances.

One operation which is a common mode of spreading contamination is evaporation of a solution to dryness either on a hot plate or under a heat lamp. It is a surprise to the novice to learn that appreciable amounts of activity may be spread in this way until he realizes that detectable amounts of contamination may represent extremely small percentages of the total sample. Consequently, all evaporations should be performed in the hood and the local hood area should be protected from the active spray by some covering such as an asbestos pad under the sample.

The experiments in this book have been designed for the most part to make use of those quantities of specific radioisotopes which the AEC has made it possible to use without receiving a specific license. For the conditions of this general license see the Federal Register, Title 10, Part 30. The requirements are as follows:

(1) Care must be exercised to avoid contamination and ingestion or inhalation of the active material.

(2) Exposure to personnel must be minimized by use of shielding and distance. Use of tongs and tweezers is recommended in handling the samples.

(3) The active material must be stored in properly labeled containers under lock and key when not in use.

The exempt quantities and nuclear properties of some nuclides are given in Appendix C. For the approved mode of disposal of these active materials, Section 20.303 of the Title 10 reference should be consulted.

In order to be certain that the personnel and area are not contaminated, it is necessary to monitor both frequently. Surveys of working areas may be made with a number of instruments depending upon the type of radiation being checked. A very satisfactory survey meter for β and γ rays is shown in Figure 5. This instrument uses a Geiger tube as the detection system. The manufacturer's instructions should be carefully followed if these instruments are to give reliable readings.

For personnel monitoring, two types of exposure devices are in common use: film badges and ionization chamber instruments such as pocket dosimeters and pocket chambers. Film badges operate by the exposure of photographic emulsion by the radiations. They are small and light, quite rugged and at the same time very sensitive. Also, the developed film provides a permanent record of the exposure. The disadvantages of photographic measurement are that the processing is time-consuming and the exact radiation value difficult to obtain as the photographic emulsion is sensitive to the energy of the radiation. Ionization chambers may be read more easily and are less energy sensitive. They are less rugged and may be discharged, giving erroneous readings, by dropping or jarring. The

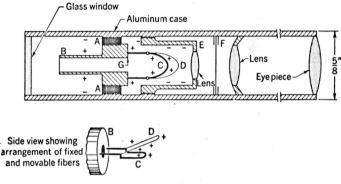

Figure 6. Pocket-dosimeter electroscope.

pocket chamber (see Figure 6) is relatively inexpensive, requiring an auxiliary "reader" instrument. Usually the chambers are calibrated to read between 0–200 milliroentgens and because of their cost and the ease of reading are excellent for a course based on this text.

Decontamination Procedures

Before beginning an experiment, the student should consider the level of activity to be handled and plan very carefully to minimize the possibility of any accident resulting in radioactive contamination of personnel, equipment, or the working area. Spilled solutions should be soaked up with tissues. The area should then be washed very well and monitored with a survey meter. If contamination can not be removed by several such washings, draw a chalk line around the area and consult the instructor. Report *all* spills to the instructor immediately.

If the hands or body should be contaminated, the area should be washed for at least 2, but not more than 3 minutes with mild soap and tepid water. Special attention should be paid to cracks, under the nails, etc. A stiff brush which might scratch should be avoided. It may be necessary to

repeat the washing several times. If soap and water are unsuccessful, then a solution prepared from equal volumes of saturated potassium permanganate solution and $0.2\ N$ sulfuric acid may be applied to the skin for no longer than 2 minutes. Then, rinse with water and apply a fresh 5% solution of sodium hydrogen sulfite for a maximum of 2 minutes. Again, this treatment may be repeated several times.

If the skin is broken by a piece of active glassware, wash the wound immediately in a strong stream of water. If ingestion of activity occurs, the treatment should be the same as for toxic chemicals and vomiting should be induced as soon as possible.

Rules and Regulations

The following rules are to be observed at all times:

(1) Pocket chambers are to be worn and the reading recorded at the end of each work session.

(2) Work areas shall be covered with paper at the start of each period and before the student leaves, the paper shall be disposed of and the area monitored with the survey meter. The paper may be either absorbent or a smooth paper like that used by butcher shops.

(3) Protective aprons, lab coats, etc. shall be left in the laboratory and not worn into the counting room.

(4) No smoking, eating, or drinking is allowed in the laboratory.

(5) Do not remove anything from the laboratory without permission. Only properly prepared counting samples are to be taken into the counting room.

(6) Contamination of counting chambers is to be avoided by every means. Taking a background count before and after counting a sample will indicate whether contamination took place.

(7) Transfer samples to and from the counting rooms only in closed containers.

(8) Wear rubber gloves when working with activity. Wash gloves well each time before removal and do not wear them outside of the laboratory. Polyethylene gloves* may be substituted. These have the advantage of being inexpensive enough to be disposed of after a single wearing.

(9) Keep micropipets in a beaker when not in use. Never pipet any solution, active or otherwise, by mouth in this laboratory.

(10) Do all evaporations, and other procedures where there is a possibility of spattering, etc., with activity, in the hood.

(11) Dispose of radioactive waste only in the special containers labeled active. Place the liquid waste in the glass containers.

* *Handguards,* Chicago Apparatus Co.

(12) Wash equipment in the sinks only if the activity level is below the background of the survey meter. Wash active equipment in the special "contaminated" cleaning solution.

(13) Wash hands thoroughly and monitor the hands, the work area and equipment before leaving the laboratory at the end of a period. Any contamination which persists after thorough cleaning is to be reported to the instructor.

EXPERIMENT 1

Use of Radiation Detection Instruments

Purpose:

To gain familiarity with the radiation detection instruments of common usage.

Method:

(1) Look over the portable survey meter, learning how to turn it on and to read it. Tape the probe down at the end of a yardstick and turn the meter on. Using a sample supplied by the instructor, take readings on the survey meter with the beta shield open and then shut, and on the position on the yardstick as the sample is moved towards the probe, along the stick. Remove the sample completely and take a background reading.

(2) Set the sample at a distance from the probe of about 5 inches or at least sufficient to get a good reading. Take readings as pieces of wood, glass, brick, and lead are placed between the sample and the probe. It is best if the pieces are of comparable thickness.

(3) With the instructor, learn how to read your pocket chamber, then to recharge it. Set it near a designated radiation source for a length of time suggested by the instructor. Take a new reading to learn the exposure dose.

Data:

Plot the reciprocal of the square root of the meter readings as a function of the distance. Discuss your observations.

PROBLEMS

1. What is the dose in rems received by a worker exposed to a field of radiation which is measured to be 50 mr for alphas, 100 mr for betas, and 150 mr for gammas? (1 mr = 0.001 rad)

2. What is the total accumulated dosage recommended as the maximum permissible by age 25, 35, 45, 60?

3. During this course experiments will be performed using Na^{22}, Sr^{90}, Cs^{137} and Pm^{147}. Based on the discussion in this chapter and the data in Appendix A, discuss these nuclides in regard to the health hazards represented, external and internal, and the type of shielding necessary.

4. What is the disintegration rate per minute of a small active source if the survey meter reads 250 mr at a distance of 2 feet? The single gamma ray has an energy of 500 kev.

5. How long may work be carried on near ($\sim$ 1 foot) to a neutron source which reads 10 mr per hour for gamma and X rays and 50 mr per hour for slow neutrons?

6. If the radiation level in a "hot" laboratory is 20 mr per hour, how many hours per week may any one individual work in it?

7. Calculate the activity in microcuries of K^{40} in a 160 pound man if the body weight is 0.35% potassium. The half life of K^{40} is 1.2×10^9 years and its isotopic abundance in natural potassium is 0.012%. Also,

$$A \text{ (disintegrations per second)} = \frac{0.693 \times \text{Number of } K^{40} \text{ atoms}}{\text{Half life in seconds}}$$

8. How many inches of lead are necessary for shielding to reduce a gamma source whose unshielded intensity is 1 roentgen at a distance of 1 foot to below 10 mr at the same distance if the energy of the gamma ray is 1 Mev? How many inches of concrete?

REFERENCES

Boursnell, J. C., *Safety Techniques for Radioactive Tracers.* London: Cambridge University Press, 1958.

Braestreys, C. B., and H. O. Wyckoff, *Radiation Protection.* Springfield, Illinois: C. C. Thomas, 1958.

Brazier, B. E., and E. K. Thompson, "Laboratories for Radioactive Research," *Architectural Record,* 216–226 (June, 1957).

Federal Register, Title 10, Part 20 and Part 30.

Garden, N. B., *Proceedings of the International Conference on the Peaceful Uses of Atomic Energy.* New York: United Nations, 7, 62 (1956).

Garden, N. B., and E. Nielsen, *Ann. Rev. Nuclear Sci.* 7, 47 (1957).

Lapp, R. E., and H. L. Andrews, *Nuclear Radiation Physics.* Englewood Cliffs, N. J.: Prentice-Hall, Inc., 1954, Chapter 17.

Novak, J. R. (ed.), *Radiation Safety Guide* (Argonne National Laboratory, ANL-5574). Washington, D. C.: Office of Technical Services, Department of Commerce, 1956.

Radiological Health Handbook. (Cincinnati: Robert A. Taft Sanitary Engineering Center.) U. S. Department of Health, Education and Welfare, 1957.

Safe Handling of Radioisotopes. New York: International Atomic Energy Agency, International Publications, Inc., 1958.

Stang, L. G., Jr., *Hot Laboratory Equipment.* Washington, D. C.: Technical Information Service, 1958.

III

Detection of Nuclear Radiation

THE knowledge which has been acquired concerning radioactivity has been gained by studying the interaction of nuclear radiations with matter. Before proceeding to a discussion of the different types of counters, it is well to consider briefly the nature of these interactions.

The three types of nuclear emissions observed from radioactive nuclides are alpha, beta, and gamma rays. All three will result from the transition from a definite nuclear energy level of the parent nucleus to a definite nuclear energy level of the daughter nucleus. Alpha and gamma emissions between two such levels will be monoenergetic. Beta emission results in ejection of a neutrino as well as an electron and the decay energy is shared between the two. As a result, instead of all the emitted beta particles for the same transition having the same energy, as alphas and gammas have, they are emitted with energies ranging from nearly zero to some maximum value close to that of the total decay energy for the transition between the two nuclear states.

Heavy Particles

In this section, the discussion will deal mainly with alpha particles. It should be realized, however, that the processes are the same for protons,

deuterons, and other heavy charged particles produced in accelerators. The alpha particle loses energy in its passage through matter by interaction of its coulombic field with those of orbital electrons. This results in dissociation of molecules or excitation and ionization of atoms or molecules of the stopping medium. The energy loss by nuclear capture or scattering is negligible compared to the electronic interaction process. The energy given up by the alpha particle in any one collision is relatively small so that many such collisions are required. Since the heavy alpha particles are monoenergetic initially, and will suffer negligible deflection in the electronic collisions, alpha particles have straight paths of rather definite lengths. A typical range curve is shown in Figure 1.

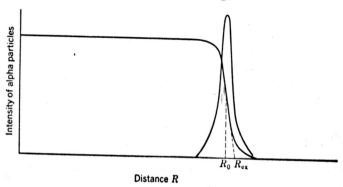

R_0 R_{ex}

Distance R

Figure 1. Range curve for alpha particles.

It is obvious that there is some variation in range. This straggling at the end of the range is a consequence of the statistical nature of the absorption process, which results in a small fluctuation in the number of collisions per unit path length and in the energy lost per collision. In addition, as the He^{2+} ion slows down at the end of its range, it can gain an electron to become He^+ which in turn may lose the electron and return briefly to the He^{2+} state or it can gain another electron to become He^0. This also introduces some straggling. The amount of straggling is indicated by the difference between R_{ex} and R_0 in Figure 1. R_{ex} is obtained from a line tangent to the curve at its inflection point; R_0 is the maximum in the differential curve; this corresponds to the value at the inflection point.

The absorption of alpha particles is studied experimentally by determining the number of ion pairs produced per unit path length. An ion pair consists of the ionized electron and the positive ion produced as a result of the ionization. The number of ion pairs per unit path length is known as the specific ionization.

This specific ionization is a measure of the rate of energy loss $\left(-\dfrac{dE}{dx}\right)$. It can be derived theoretically that

$$-\frac{dE}{dx} \propto \frac{1}{v^2} \qquad v = \text{velocity of alpha particle} \qquad \text{(III-1)}$$

This is shown to be valid experimentally in Figure 2 (a Bragg curve). This relationship is reasonable as the alpha particle takes a longer time to pass through a unit length as v decreases so the probability of interaction should increase. It can also be demonstrated that $\left(-\dfrac{dE}{dx}\right)$ is proportional to Z, the atomic number of the absorber.

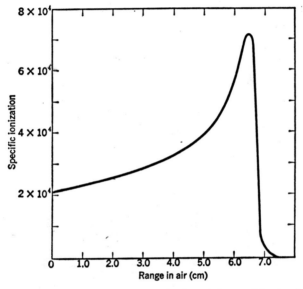

Figure 2. Specific ionization of 7.7 Mev alpha particles in air.

For most gases it has been found experimentally that about 34 ev is lost per ion pair. For solids and liquids the energy loss is closer to 5 ev per ion pair. Table I lists the value for w, the average loss per ion pair in a number of substances.

TABLE I

Average Energy Loss Per Ion Pair

Gas	Particle	w (ev)	Gas	Particle	w (ev)
Air[1]	Electron	32.0	Helium[2]	Alpha	42.7
Air[1]	Proton	36.0	Neon[2]	Alpha	36.8
Air[2]	Alpha	35.5	Argon[2]	Alpha	26.4
Hydrogen[2]	Alpha	36.3	Methane[2]	Alpha	29.4

[1] L. H. Gray, *Proc. Cambridge Phil. Soc.*, **40**, 72 (1944).
[2] N. P. Jesse, and J. Sadauskis, *Phys. Rev.*, **90**, 1120 (1953).

For alpha particles between 4 and 7 Mev the range in air is given by the equation

$$R_{(cm)} = 0.309E^{3/2}_{(Mev)} \qquad \text{(III-2)}$$

The range in other materials can be approximated by

$$R_A = 0.173E^{3/2}A^{1/3} \qquad \text{(III-3)}$$

where $E = E_\alpha$ in Mev,
   A = atomic weight of absorber,
   R_A = range in absorber expressed in units of mg per cm^2.

The unit of mg per cm^2 is commonly used in range-energy measurements and is obtained by multiplying the thickness of the absorber by the density. (See Figure 3.)

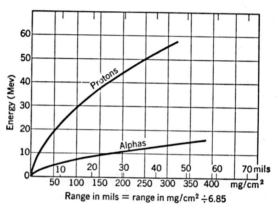

Figure 3. Range in aluminum (mg/cm^2 and mils).

With the exception of electrons and gamma rays, the range of particles other than alphas can be rather well estimated from the relation

$$R_x = R_\alpha \left(\frac{M_x}{M_\alpha}\right)\left(\frac{Z_\alpha}{Z_x}\right)^2 - C \qquad \text{(III-4)}$$

This equation is valid only for the case of equal velocities for the particle x and the alpha particle. Therefore, to calculate the range of a proton of energy E_p, it is necessary to know the range of an alpha particle of energy E_α such that $v_p = v_\alpha$. To have equivalence of velocities, the relationship of the two energies must be

$$E_\alpha = E_p \left(\frac{M_\alpha}{M_p}\right) \qquad \text{(III-5)}$$

If $Z_x = Z_\alpha$, then $C = 0$; if $2Z_x = Z_\alpha$, then $C = 0.20$ cm.

In the case of fission fragments, the experimental range energy curve is shown in Figure 4. The initial charge is around 20, but as the fission fragment slows to a velocity less than the orbital velocity of the next electron to be gained, it will gain this electron. The result will be a continual de-

crease in charge throughout the range and not just in the last few milli-
meters as for alpha particles. This continually changing charge accounts
for the curve in Figure 4. Also, the higher charges through most of the

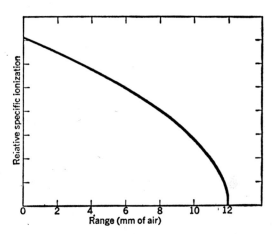

Figure 4. Range curve for fission fragments.

range will favor much greater nuclear scattering by the absorber nuclei.
This effect is in such a direction that it also produces a curve of the type
shown. Fission fragment ranges in air are about 1.9 to 2.9 cm as compared
to approximately 5 to 6 cm in air for alpha particles emitted by heavy
radioactive nuclides.

Electrons

Electrons lose their energy in basically the same fashion as heavy particles; however, some very important differences do exist. Since the mass of
the electron is so small, for the same energy the velocity will be very much
greater than that of a heavy particle. As a result, since the same dependence on velocity exists, i.e.

$$\left(-\frac{dE}{dx}\right) \propto \frac{1}{v^2},$$

the specific ionization per unit path length will be much less than for heavy
particles. Because of its smaller mass, an electron may lose a large fraction
of its energy in one collision. This fact means that the statistical treatment
can not be expected to be as valid for electrons as for heavy ions since
large deviations from the average will occur frequently. The average loss
per ion pair formed is still approximately 32 ev for many gases, including
air. When an abnormally large amount of energy is lost in a particular
collision, the primary electron will be deflected through a larger angle.
These large angle deflections will result in widely different apparent path

lengths in the forward direction for individual electrons from a common source. Any one electron may suffer several such large deflections and eventually be scattered again in the forward direction or even in the backward direction (Figure 5). The electrons produced in the ion pair forma-

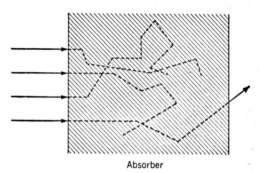

Absorber

Figure 5. Electron paths in an absorber.

tion may themselves have relatively high energies transferred to them and they in turn will cause secondary ion pair formation as they lose their energy. In fact, the primary electrons account for only 20 to 30% of the total ionization. Nuclear scattering is a more important factor for electrons than it is for heavy particles. This scattering is related directly to the loss of energy through radiation when a fast moving electron is accelerated in the field of a nucleus. The radiation energy lost is known as bremsstrahlung and is in the form of X rays. The ratio between the energy loss by radiation and that by ionization and excitation is given by

$$\frac{(dE/dx)_R}{(dE/dx)_I} = \frac{EZ}{800} \qquad\qquad \text{(III-6)}$$

From this it can be seen that an electron of 10 Mev energy will lose energy at approximately equal rates by both processes when lead ($Z = 82$) is used for the absorber. Loss of energy by radiation can occur for heavy particles in the same manner but in order to have sufficiently high velocities for it to be significant, the particles must have energies on the order of a few hundred million electron volts.

The final complication with electrons arises from the fact that while it is possible to obtain monoenergetic electrons by various means, natural beta decay does not yield either monoenergetic electrons or positrons. Because of the simultaneous emission of a neutrino, the beta particles are emitted with a spectrum of energies (Figure 6). In negatron decay the average energy is approximately $\frac{1}{3}E_{max}$ whereas in positron emission, it is approximately $\frac{2}{3}E_{max}$. Since several beta groups, each with its own energy spectrum may be emitted by a particular nuclide, it is easy to realize that the initial source of electrons will be very dissimilar from the monoenergetic

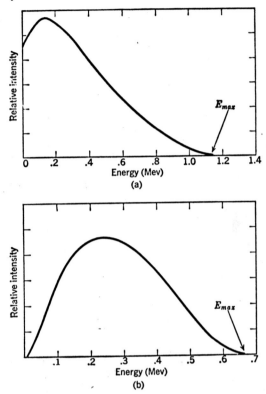

Figure 6. (a) Energy spectrum for β^+ rays from a positron emitter. (b) Energy spectrum for β^- rays from a negatron emitter.

alpha particles in the previous discussion. When the spectrum of path lengths for any one energy is superimposed on the spectrum of energies, it is not surprising that range straggling of 15–20% is observed. Since so few beta particles have the maximum energy, it is difficult to determine with precision an exact range. In Chapter V further consideration is given to range-energy relations for beta particles.

Electromagnetic Radiation

In nuclear science two sources of electromagnetic radiation are of interest, gamma rays and X rays. The former have their origin in the nucleus and are emitted when energetically excited nuclei decay to a lower energy level. This de-excitation emission of gamma rays is analogous to the emission of X rays which occurs when a transition takes place between an excited atomic state and one of lower energy. Since nuclei exist in discrete energy levels, a de-excitation process will occur between two such levels and the

resulting gamma ray will have a definite, discrete energy. X-ray energies are usually on the order of 0–50 kev while gamma-ray energies range from several kev to several Mev. The mode of interaction with matter will be the same for X rays as for gamma rays and is a strong function of the energy. The average specific ionization will be only $\frac{1}{10}$ to $\frac{1}{100}$ as great as for electrons and, consequently, practically all the ionization by gamma rays is secondary in nature arising from the ionization produced by the stopping of the primary ion pairs.

There are three mechanisms for the interaction of gamma rays or X rays with matter.

(1) Photoelectric Effect: The photon interacts with the absorber atom as a whole and is completely absorbed. As a result of this energy absorption, a "photoelectron" is ejected from an inner orbital with an energy whose value is given by Equation (III-7).

$$E_{e^-} = E_\gamma - E_{B.E.} \qquad \text{(III-7)}$$

where E_{e^-} = energy of photoelectron,
       E_γ = energy of gamma ray absorbed,
       $E_{B.E.}$ = binding energy of ejected electron.

The photoelectron in turn is degraded in energy by the processes described in the preceding section. The vacancy in an inner orbital will result in electrons from higher levels falling down to fill all

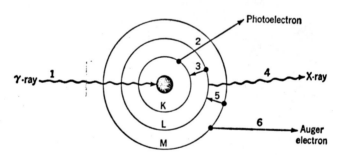

Figure 7. Photoelectric effect and its consequences.

the lower vacancies (Figure 7, Nos. 3 and 5). X rays characteristic of the absorber will be emitted with energies equal to the difference in binding energies of the two electronic levels involved in the transition (No. 4). In place of an X ray, a low energy electron, known as an Auger electron may be emitted (No. 6).

(2) Compton Scattering: If the energy of the gamma ray is sufficiently large, rather than interaction with the atom as a whole, the gamma ray may interact with any one of the orbital electrons as though it were essentially a free electron. The electron will be ejected, creat-

ing an ion pair, and the gamma ray will be scattered with an energy given by

$$E_{\gamma_t} = E_{\gamma_i} - E_{\text{B.E.}_{e^-}} \tag{III-8}$$

If the ejected electron is from an inner orbital, X-ray and Auger-electron emission will result, as described for the photoelectric effect. (See Figure 8.)

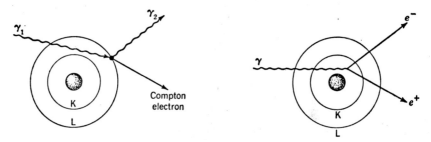

Figure 8. Compton scattering.   **Figure 9.** Pair production.

Since E_{γ_t} will depend on the angle of deflection, a spectrum of scattered Compton radiation results. The Compton electrons will likewise have a spectrum of energies.

(3) Pair Production: When the energy of the gamma is very high, the gamma ray may be converted in the coulombic field of a nucleus into a negatron and a positron. Since two electronic masses are formed, at least an energy equivalent to this (i.e., 2 × 0.51 = 1.02 Mev) is required. If the initial gamma-ray energy is greater than this threshold value, the excess will appear as kinetic energy of the pair. The negatron will be degraded as described earlier. The positron will exist only until it slows down sufficiently to interact with another negatron to "annihilate" the pair, producing annihilation radiation quanta of 0.51 Mev. This annihilation process is the reverse, then, of pair production.

Since, except in Compton scattering, each gamma ray will be removed from a beam by a single event, it is not correct in a strict sense to speak of a range.

The photoelectric effect is the predominant mode of interaction in aluminum for gamma rays below 60 kev and in lead below 600 kev. The Compton effect is the major mode for photon energies between 60 kev and 15 Mev in aluminum and 600 kev and 5 Mev in lead. Pair production predominates above the energy range for the Compton effect. (See Figures 10 and 11.)

Frequently, rather than emit a gamma ray, a nucleus will interact with its external electronic shells and cause emission of an electron with an

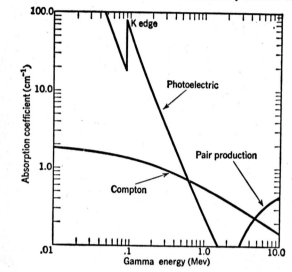

Figure 10. Dependence of absorption coefficients for lead on energy.

energy given by

$$E_{e^-} = E_\gamma - E_{\text{B.E.}} \tag{III-9}$$

where E_γ = energy of expected gamma ray,
$E_{\text{B.E.}}$ = binding energy of the electron.

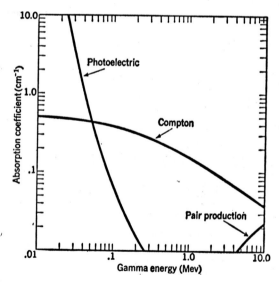

Figure 11. Dependence of absorption coefficients for aluminum on energy.

This process is known as internal conversion and these electrons as conversion electrons. In the case where the gamma-ray emission was subsequent to beta decay, the monoenergetic conversion electrons will appear as a spike on the beta energy spectrum. X-ray and Auger-electron emission will accompany these conversion electrons.

In decay by the process of electron capture, no nuclear particle is emitted, but gamma rays, conversion electrons, X rays and Auger electrons may all be emitted. In isomeric transitions where a nucleus in an excited metastable state decays to the ground state, all these radiations may again be seen.

Detection Systems

All the detection systems used for nuclear radiations depend upon the interaction of the electric field of the moving particle with the detector material to produce ionization, or, in the case of neutral emissions such as gamma rays and neutrons, upon the ionization produced by secondary processes. In this chapter the operational characteristics and the advantages and disadvantages of the several types of detectors using a gas as the sensitive medium are discussed. In addition to the detector wherein the radiation produces ionization, every detection system must also include a measuring part which receives the output of the detector and translates it into useful information. The component parts of this measuring apparatus are described briefly but not in any way intended to make the student of this text equipped to deal with the electronic intricacies of such systems.

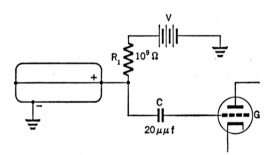

Figure 12

Two basic modes of operation exist for detection systems. In the pulse-type operation the output of the detector is a series of pulses separated in time. Each pulse is the product of interaction of a nuclear radiation with the detector. The experiments at the end of this chapter use the pulse-type counting systems. If the pulses are not separated, but rather the system averages over many interactions, then a count-rate meter operation (such as used in Chapter VIII, Experiment 17) results.

Since in passage through matter of radiation, ion pairs are formed consisting of electrons and positive ions, this ionization may be used to detect the radiation by collecting the charges on appropriate electrodes. The small, very mobile electrons are rapidly collected on the anode (the center wire in Figure 12) which is maintained at a high positive potential above ground by the high voltage power supply V. The resistance R_1 allows the voltage to drop on the central wire upon collection of electrons as it isolates the power supply from the wire. This potential decrease is only momentary as the wire will be recharged by V (Figure 13). The time necessary to

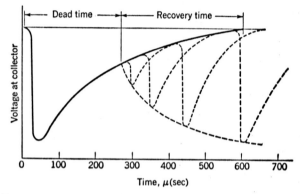

Figure 13. Illustration of dead time in a typical Geiger tube. [H. G. Stever, *Phys. Rev.*, **61**, 38 (1942)]

restore the original potential will be a function of the decrease in the electric field near the wire due to the buildup of a sheath of slow moving positive ions. The voltage pulse, which will be negative since the wire was positively charged is imposed on the grid of a vacuum tube (G) after transmission through the capacitor C. The resulting current flow is registered ultimately as a count.

In Figure 14, the number of ion pairs collected is shown as a function of the voltage between the two collecting electrodes. In Region II of the curve, a flat plateau over a relatively wide range of voltage is seen. Prior to the attainment of the threshold voltage for the plateau, the ions (by ions, both electrons and positive ions will be meant) did not have sufficient drift velocity in the field to prevent elimination of some ion pairs by recombination. Throughout the plateau range, the drift velocity is sufficient to make recombination negligible. Ionization chambers operate in this voltage region. In Region III, the electrons from the primary ion pairs receive enough acceleration to produce additional ionization, and the process of gas multiplication increases the number of collected charges. This is the region of proportional counter operation, as the pulses are proportional in size to the energy deposited in the detector by the passage of

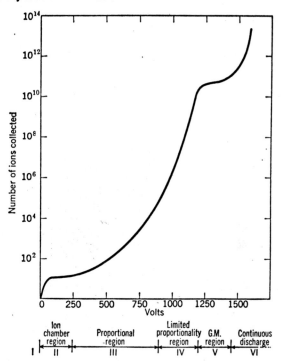

Figure 14. The number of ion-pairs formed, as a function of detector voltage.

the initial radiation. Region V is that used for Geiger-Müller counter operation. Here the gas multiplication is very high, and the pulse size is completely independent of the initial ionization. Beyond Region V, continuous discharge of the detector counting tube occurs.

Ionization Chambers

These counters have the advantage of being simple, dependable and rugged. They have the disadvantage of supplying only a very small voltage pulse and hence require a large amount of external amplification for pulse type operation. Usually of parallel plate construction, they have been used frequently for alpha particle detection. Modified ionization chambers are used to obtain accurate energy measurements of alpha particles. The pocket chambers mentioned in Chapter II are ionization chambers.

Proportional Counters

The electric field strength of an electrode at a distance r from the electrode is proportional to $1/r$. This has very important application for detec-

tor chambers of cylindrical construction with one electrode (the cathode) the cylinder itself and the other (the anode) an axial wire. If the applied voltage of a cylindrical chamber of 1 cm radius is 1000 volts, the potential in the immediate vicinity of a center wire of 1 mil (0.001 inches) diameter will be about 7×10^4 volts/cm. As the primary electrons reach the vicinity of this high field and increase their kinetic energy, they will produce secondary ionization and so increase the pulse detected at the wire anode. Since this multiplication occurs only in the immediate vicinity of the center wire, there will be little chance for tertiary ionization. Tertiary electrons may be produced by photoemission resulting from the photons of the secondary ionization process.

M is defined by

$$M = \text{gas multiplication factor} \qquad \text{(III-10)}$$

$$= \frac{\text{number electrons collected}}{\text{number electrons in primary ionization}}$$

Values of M of 10^3 to 10^5 are commonly achieved in proportional counter operation. If $M = 10^3$, then essentially all the gas multiplication occurs within 10 mean-free-path lengths for the electron in the gas from the wire

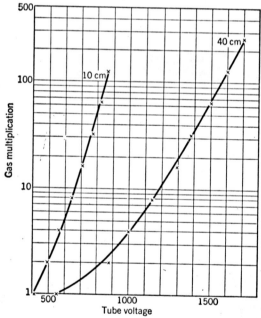

Figure 15. Gas multiplication M as a function of voltage, **for** pressure of 10 and 40 cm Hg, argon 99.6 per cent pure; collector diameter, 0.01 in.; cathode diameter, 0.87 in. [B. B. Rossi and H. H. Staub, "Ionization Chambers and Counters," *National Nuclear Energy Series,* vol. 2, McGraw-Hill (1949)]

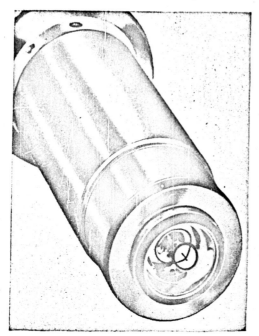

Figure 16. Windowless flow counter: photograph of a chamber and a schematic diagram of a chamber mounted in the shield; the micromil window (150 μg/cm²) is optional. (*Courtesy Nuclear-Chicago Corp.*)

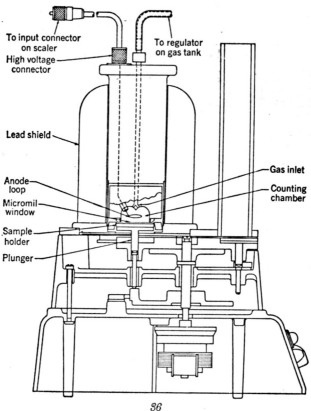

To input connector on scaler

High voltage connector

To regulator on gas tank

Lead shield

Anode loop

Micromil window

Sample holder

Plunger

Gas inlet

Counting chamber

(2^{10} = 1024). Since at one atmosphere, the mean-free-path length is approximately 10^{-4} cm, the gas multiplication occurs in the last 0.01 mm next to the wire. Figure 15 shows the variation of M with applied voltage. For a given voltage, the detector pulse output will be directly proportional to the primary ionization, since M is a constant factor by which all amounts of primary ionization are increased. This makes it possible to use the proportional counter to distinguish between alpha particles and beta particles, or even between similar particles of different energies, since different amounts of primary ionization will be produced.

The output pulse in proportional counter operation depends only on the collection of the electrons and not on the positive ions. Consequently, the rate of detection depends on the time necessary for the primary electrons to drift into the region of high field strength near the anode wire. This makes it a much faster counter than the ion chambers which depend on the slow moving positive ions. It can also handle much higher count rates than a Geiger-Müller counter. In fact, the detector tube can amplify another pulse before the earlier positive ion cloud has moved very far if the new ionization occurs at a different location on the wire. Time intervals necessary to enable the counter to measure two distinct pulses (the resolving time) can be as low as 0.2 to 0.5 microsecond. Frequently, the associated electronic measuring apparatus limits the resolving time rather than the detector itself. For accurate use of a proportional counter for particle energy measurements, any residual positive ion cloud must have time to drift an appreciable distance before a new pulse is amplified. In this case, intervals between pulses of 100 microseconds are used.

Counting gases are usually one of the noble gases mixed with a small amount of a polyatomic gas. The latter makes the gas multiplication factor less dependent on applied voltage, possibly by suppressing the tertiary photoemission. They also increase the speed of electron collection by suppression of the resonant Ramsauer effect. P-gas (90% A and 10% CH_4) and Q-gas (96% He and 4% i-C_4H_{10}) are mixtures supplied commercially. The gas mixture and the electrodes may be separated by a thin window from the radioactive sample (Figure 16) or the counter may be operated windowless. For windowless operation, the chamber is flushed with gas after insertion of the sample and, also, the anode wire is frequently a loop (Figure 17). It is necessary in flushing to sweep out all oxygen and water vapor, as these molecules absorb electrons readily to form negative ions and in so doing, reduce the pulse size. For alpha and beta particles whose range does not exceed the dimensions of the chamber, windowless counters are often referred to as 2π counters since a solid angle of 2π is subtended above the sample. If proper care is taken, the count rate will be very close to 50% of the true disintegration rate. These windowless proportional counters are very useful for measuring low energy radiations such as the beta particles of carbon-14 and tritium.

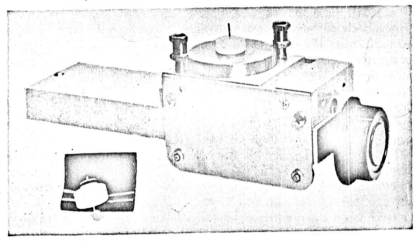

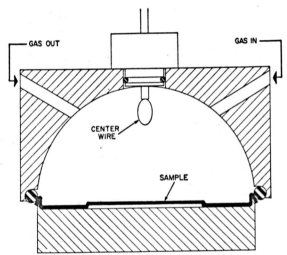

Figure 17. Windowless flow chamber: photograph and schematic diagram. (*Courtesy Nuclear Measurements Corp.*)

Geiger-Müller Counters

As the voltage is increased beyond that of the proportional region, the feature of proportionality between the primary ionization and the output pulse disappears and the latter becomes the same size for all initial ionization whether it be a 6 Mev alpha particle or a 50 kev X ray. This fact means that a counter operating in such a way will have certain advantages. These Geiger-Müller counters have high sensitivity to all different kinds of radiation and the large size of the output pulse (from one volt to tens,

of volts compared to the several tenths of a millivolt output of ionization chambers) requires much less external amplification, considerably reducing the complexity and cost of the auxiliary electronic equipment. The detector tubes for Geiger-Müller counters are quite simple and allow a great deal of flexibility in design. However, as a counterbalance to these advantages, Geiger-Müller counters are limited to handling lower count rates than proportional counters.

As with proportional region operation, the primary electrons cause secondary ionization near the center anode wire. This initial avalanche ends when these very mobile electrons are all collected by the anode, but a succession of further avalanches is triggered by the photoelectrons from the previous avalanche. Thus, the avalanches will spread along the complete length of the wire and will continue until the buildup of the positive ion sheath progresses to a point sufficient to reduce the field strength enough to prevent further ionization. This buildup takes place because the heavy positive ions have such a slow rate of movement that they are essentially stationary during the time interval of the electron avalanches. The time necessary to reach this point in the process is of the order of a few microseconds. The positive ion sheath slowly drifts to the cathode where it may induce new avalanches by producing photoelectrons in the process of extracting electrons from the cathode to neutralize itself. To avoid a recurring pulsing which would render the counter useless it is necessary to prevent further avalanches at this point by the process of quenching. The tube may be quenched externally by changing the field at the critical moment but it is far more common to use internal quenching. Usually a small amount of an organic compound such as ethyl alcohol or ethyl formate is included in the counting gas as a quencher. Since the ionization potential of the organic molecule is lower than that of argon, the usual counting gas, as the argon positive ion sheath moves to the cathode and encounters organic molecules, the reaction (III-11) occurs.

$$A^+ + (EtOH)^0 \longrightarrow A^0 + (EtOH)^+ \qquad \text{(III-11)}$$

As a result, only positive organic ions reach the cathode. The energy involved in neutralization in this case serves to excite the organic molecule and to dissociate it into uncharged fragments rather than produce electron emission. The tube remains inactive for several hundred microseconds during the initial drift of the positive ion sheath from the anode wire. As the sheath continues to move away and the field strength near the anode increases, the counter will operate but with smaller output pulses for approximately the same length of time (Figure 13).

Geiger-Müller tubes are available commercially from many firms in a very wide variety of shapes and sizes. Tubes have been used successfully varying from approximately one mm to several cm in diameter and from one cm to several feet in length. Frequently the cathode is made by coat-

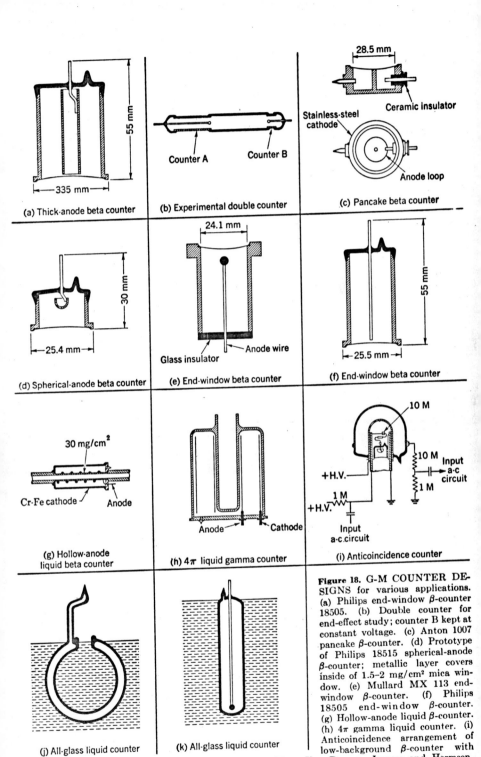

(a) Thick-anode beta counter

(b) Experimental double counter

Counter A   Counter B

(c) Pancake beta counter

Stainless-steel cathode

Ceramic insulator

Anode loop

(d) Spherical-anode beta counter

(e) End-window beta counter

Glass insulator   Anode wire

(f) End-window beta counter

30 mg/cm²

Cr-Fe cathode   Anode

(g) Hollow-anode liquid beta counter

Anode   Cathode

(h) 4π liquid gamma counter

+H.V.

+H.V.

Input a-c circuit

10 M

10 M   Input a-c circuit

1 M

(i) Anticoincidence counter

(j) All-glass liquid counter

(k) All-glass liquid counter

Figure 18. G-M COUNTER DE-SIGNS for various applications. (a) Philips end-window β-counter 18505. (b) Double counter for end-effect study; counter B kept at constant voltage. (c) Anton 1007 pancake β-counter. (d) Prototype of Philips 18515 spherical-anode β-counter; metallic layer covers inside of 1.5–2 mg/cm² mica window. (e) Mullard MX 113 end-window β-counter. (f) Philips 18505 end-window β-counter. (g) Hollow-anode liquid β-counter. (h) 4π gamma liquid counter. (i) Anticoincidence arrangement of low-background β-counter with guard counter. (j) and (k) All-glass liquid counters. (From Van Duuren, Jaspers and Hermsen, *Nucleonics*, 17, 86 (June, 1959).

ing the inside of a glass cylinder with a conducting material, e.g., a metal or graphite, while the anode may be a tungsten wire 3 to 4 mils in diameter mounted coaxially. The end window tube (Figure 18c) has a thin mica window, and the center wire is terminated with a glass bead to prevent sparking between it and the walls because of the high potential difference. As is usual in all detector systems, the cathode is at ground potential while the anode is at a high positive potential. The counting gas may be argon, neon, or nitrogen with approximately 10% of an impurity quencher such as ethyl alcohol. The total pressure will be 7 to 15 cm of Hg. The lifetime of tube is limited by the fact that the organic quencher is destroyed gradually (see Problem 6). Halogen quenchers which are not destroyed are used, but these give the tube poorer characteristics in other respects.

Semiconductor Detectors

The use of semiconductor diode devices as detectors for ionizing radiations is a relatively young field but one which is very rapidly growing as insight is gained into the nature of their operation and fabrication. If a voltage is applied to a diode, an electric field is established at the junction between the two semiconductor materials. This creates a small volume on both sides of the junction (the depletion layer) in which charges generated by the passage of radiation are swept apart and attracted to the two terminals. The diode is in a sense acting as a solid-state ionization chamber with two important differences from the more familiar gas-filled detector: (1) the density is much greater so the range of heavy particles (alphas, etc.) is in microns rather than centimeters; (2) only 3.5 ev is required to produce an ion-pair (in this case, an electron-hole pair) in silicon as compared to 28 ev in argon. As a result, in a very much smaller volume, for the same total energy deposited, approximately 8 times as much charge is generated in the solid-state detector as in the gas-filled ionization chamber. The semiconductor detectors, at present, are made from thin (approximately 1 mm) wafers of semiconductor silicon. The diode is prepared from this in one of two ways. If p-type silicon (silicon containing acceptor impurities which create electron deficient holes in the silicon crystal) is used, a small amount of a donor material such as phosphorous is diffused into the silicon to produce a thin n-type region (one which contains an excess of donor impurities thereby supplying semi-free electrons in this region). If n-type silicon is used, a thin p-type layer is produced by evaporating a small amount of gold onto the silicon surface after it has been chemically etched. Detectors with detection areas between 5 mm² and 2 cm² are available. It is reasonable to expect that as the technology increases, greater sensitive volumes (larger areas and thicker depletion layers) will be produced with various semiconductor materials. At present the major use is in alpha and fission fragment detection as their ranges are comparable to the thickness of the depletion layer. Alpha particle energy analysis by these devices surpasses in resolution that possible by gas-filled ionization chambers and since the semiconductor detectors are much more rugged and simpler to use, they are replacing ionization chambers for alpha particle detection and analysis. Their importance in beta particle detection will increase as devices with thicker depletion layers are developed. As these detectors become generally available, it would be worthwhile considering their use in the experiments requiring alpha particle detection.

Measuring System

The total electronic system necessary to obtain useful information about a nuclear radiation is shown in block diagram in Figure 19.

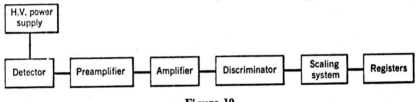

Figure 19

The high voltage power supply furnishes the potential difference necessary for the detector to collect ions. The output pulse of the detector will vary in size from a few hundred microvolts to volts depending upon the amount, if any, of gas amplification. The smaller the output pulse, the greater the external amplification required. The preamplifier is mounted close to the detector physically and serves to provide a small initial gain (of 10 to 100) for systems needing high total gain. Also, this initial amplification serves to overcome the pulse attenuation which results from passage through the connecting cable (due to the capacitance of the cable).

The amplifier is a very important part of the system and should be chosen carefully with respect to the type and mode of counting desired. The total gain (amplification) in a system may vary from 10 for Geiger-Müller operation to 10^4 for ionization chambers. A limit is set on the voltage gain of an amplifier by the presence of electronic "noise" at the amplifier input. This "noise" is due to stray fields, microphonics, and defective components resulting in small random voltage changes. These will be amplified also and will mask small input pulses. Some of the noise may be eliminated by proper design and maintenance of the electronic circuitry but a small inherent noise mainly due to the random nature of electron emission by the cathode of electronic tubes can not be eliminated. The signal-to-noise ratio is the ratio of output pulse for a given input signal to the noise level at the output.

The discriminator serves to allow only pulses above a certain size to be passed on to the rest of the system. By this means, "noise" pulses can be rejected. In the case of proportional counters the smaller pulses from beta particles can be discriminated against in the presence of the larger alpha pulses when the count rate for the latter alone is desired.

The discriminator passes on output pulses of uniform size and shape. The scaling system selects every nth pulse to pass on to the mechanical registers. Binary systems (where n is a power of 2) were used quite widely, but in recent years they have been replaced by decade systems. The mechanical registers are much too slow for most counting rates directly and in order that their operation not be the limiting rate in counting, they may register only every 100th or 1000th count. The interval counts between 0 and the register scale factor is shown by neon lights.

Experimental

In the following experiments the operating characteristics of a Geiger and a proportional counter are studied. This is done by measuring the count rate of a sample as a function of the counter voltage. If the detectors are in useful condition, over a certain range of voltages, there will be little change in count rate. This is the counter plateau. For optimum operation the voltage is maintained within this range, usually near the middle. This prevents small fluctuations in the line voltage from affecting the count rate to any significant degree. Frequently, in Geiger-Müller counters the operating voltage is chosen to be one third of the distance from the plateau threshold, rather than one half. This still provides insensitivity to line voltage changes but also, since the detector pulses (gas amplification) are smaller, the lifetime of the organic quencher is prolonged. Follow the directions for operation of the counters very carefully as these are expensive instruments (a Geiger tube costs about $75 alone) and can be damaged easily. For example, Geiger tubes become light sensitive if the window is scratched; also, prolonged operation at voltages beyond the plateau in the region of continuous discharges quickly depletes the quencher and so ruins the tube. Care must be taken at all times when counting radioactivity that the counting chamber does not become contaminated through careless handling of a sample. Two sample stands are shown in Figure 20.

In addition to the determination of the plateau range, for the Geiger counter two other measurements will be made. It was mentioned above that a Geiger tube remains inactive for some time after a pulse before a new radiation can cause a new pulse. The minimum time necessary to count two successive radiations is known as the resolving time. Since radioactive decay is a statistical, random process and not one evenly spaced in time, even at relatively low count rates a certain percentage of the events will occur within the resolving time of the counting system.

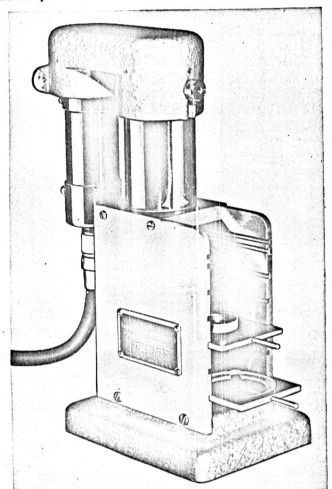

Figure 20 (a). End-window Geiger tube mount and sample holder. (*Courtesy Tracerlab, Inc.*)

In order to get the true count rate, it is necessary to know the correction that must be made for this coincidence loss. Letting τ represent the resolving time, m the observed count rate, and n the true count rate, then

$$n - m = nm\tau \qquad \text{(III-12)}$$

and

$$n = \frac{m}{1 - m\tau} \qquad \text{(III-13)}$$

In this experiment the method of matched samples is used. Two samples of sufficiently low counting rates that the coincidence losses are negligible

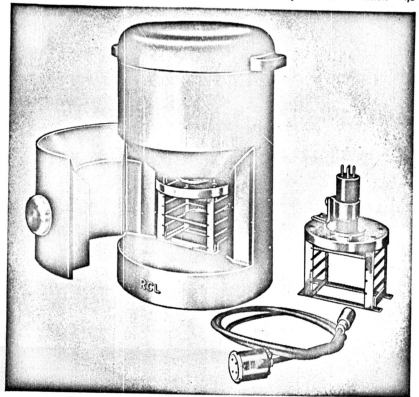

Figure 20 (b). End-window Geiger tube mount and sample holder enclosed by a lead shield. (*Courtesy Radiation Counter Laboratories.*)

are counted separately, then together. The two samples should have approximately the same count rate. From the difference between the measured count rate of the pair together and the sum of their individual rates, the resolving time is calculated. In Geiger-Müller counters, the resolving time is that of the tube; for proportional counters, the detector and the electronic system have about the same resolving time.

The final part of this experiment is a measure of count rate as a function of distance between sample and detector to study the relationship between the two.

EXPERIMENT 2

Geiger-Müller Counters

Purpose:

To study the characteristics of Geiger counter operation.

Method:

Part I. *Plateau*

(1) Turn on the power switch and wait 30 seconds, then turn on the high voltage switch.

(2) After another 30-second wait, insert the sample obtained from the instructor into the holder.

(3) Bring the H. V. to approximately 700 volts with the coarse adjustment and then use the fine adjustment to make it exactly 700 volts. Count

Date: _____			Voltage: _____				
Isotopes: _____			Discriminator: _____				
_____			Background/5 min: _____				
_____			Background/min: _____				
Time started: _____			Time finished: _____				

Sample	Counting time	Total counts	cpm	Avg. cpm	Background	Net avg. cpm	Notes

Figure 21. Typical counting data form.

for 0.5 minute intervals each 100 volt increment until an increase in count rate is obtained. Then count for one minute intervals at each 50 volt increment until a large increase in count rate is noted. Record all data on a form such as Figure 21. Record the discriminator setting and the number of the Geiger-Müller tube and scalar.

(4) Turn off the H. V. but not the power switch when the experiment is completed. Geiger-Müller tubes will continue to age even when the count switch is off unless the H. V. is turned off.

Data:

Plot the counts per minute (cpm) versus the voltage. Calculate the slope and width of the plateau. For a useful tube, the plateau should extend at least 100 volts with a slope of less than 7%. For future use of the tube, record the optimum operating voltage (approximately one third the width from the threshold voltage).

Part II. *Resolving Time*

(1) Take a background (i.e. one with no sample) count for 10 minutes.
(2) Obtain two semicircular sources from the instructor. Position source A on the proper shelf in the holder to obtain between 6000 to 12,000 cpm and count for 10 minutes.

(3) Without moving source A, place source B next to it and count for 10 minutes.

(4) Remove source A without disturbing B and count B alone for 10 minutes.

Data:

After subtracting the background, calculate the resolving time using these data and Equation (III-13). Then, using the value of τ obtained, calculate n for a sufficient number of values of m ranging from 2000 to 30,000 to draw a good curve of n versus m. This curve may be used throughout the course if the same Geiger-Müller tube is used.

Part III. *Geometry*

(1) Count source A on each shelf of the sample holder.
(2) Measure the distance between the shelves accurately. In this experiment, as at any other time, avoid physical contact with the tube window.

Data:

After correcting the data for coincidence losses, plot cpm versus distance from the first shelf on log-log paper and discuss the observations. Be sure to subtract background before plotting.

EXPERIMENT 3

Proportional Counters

Purpose:

To measure the plateaus of a proportional counter for alpha and beta rays.

Method:

If the detector is a thin window counter, then disregard the instructions below concerning flushing. For a windowless chamber, it is necessary to flush sufficiently before counting.

(1) Turn the scalar and proportional counter convertor on at least 5 minutes prior to use. With the purge control closed, open the gas cylinder valves to 10 pounds. Insert a uranium sample obtained from the instructor carefully into the chamber, close and flush the chamber with a moderately high gas flow rate for two minutes. A Ra D-E-F standard (National Bureau of Standards) may be used in place of the uranium standard. After this, turn the gas flow down to about a bubble per second.

(2) Beginning with the high voltage set at 600 volts, take a 0.5 minute count every 50 to 100 volts as required to define the plateau adequately. Continue until 2200 volts or until the second (beta) plateau is passed. Take a 5 minute background at the proper voltages (the midpoint of the plateaus) for alphas and betas.

Data:

Plot the cpm versus voltage and discuss this curve and its interpretation by proportional counting theory.

PROBLEMS

1. If the efficiency for a Geiger tube is $1 - e^{-N}$ where N is the number of primary ion pairs, calculate the efficiency for $N = 1, 2, 3, 4$, and 5. What does this tell you about the relative efficiency of Geiger-Müller counters for alpha, beta, and gamma rays (assuming they penetrate the window)?

2. The equation for the pulse size in a detector operating in the proportional region is

$$\Delta V = M \frac{ne}{c}$$

where M = gas multiplication factor,
   n = number of electrons from the primary ionization,
   e = electronic charge,
   c = capacitance of the counter.

Assume reasonable values of M and n, set c equal to 50 micromicrofarads, and calculate the ΔV for a 1 Mev beta particle.

3. What is the total charge released when Cm^{244} emits a 5.8 Mev alpha particle in an ionization chamber with air at 1 atm as the counting gas?

4. What is the range of a 5 Mev proton in aluminum?

5. What is the minimum energy that an alpha particle must have to be counted in a Geiger tube with a mica window of 1.0 mg/cm^2 thickness?

6. Assume that 10^9 alcohol molecules will be dissociated per discharge in a Geiger tube of 100 cm^3 volume filled with 90% argon and 10% ethyl alcohol vapor. The total pressure at 25°C is 10 cm of Hg. What will be the lifetime of the tube in terms of total counts (assuming this coincides with the complete dissociation of the alcohol molecules)?

7. If it is desired to bombard a target with 25 Mev alpha particles using a cyclotron which produces an alpha beam of 40 Mev energy, what is the thickness (in mils) of the aluminum foil which should be placed in front of the target? Density of aluminum is 2.70 g per cm^3.

8. The electron binding energies in aluminum are: K-shell = 1560 ev; L-shell = 87 ev; M-shell = 6 ev. What will be the energy of the photoelectrons seen in the absorption of Ba-137m gamma rays?

9. The electron binding energies in barium are: K-shell = 37.4 kev; L-shell = 6.0 kev; M-shell = 1.30 kev. What will be the energy of the conversion electrons seen in the decay of Ba-137m? Compare this with the answers of Problem 8.

REFERENCES

Evans, R. D., *The Atomic Nucleus.* New York: McGraw-Hill Book Co., Inc., 1955, Chapters 21–25.

Fretter, William B., *Introduction to Experimental Physics.* Englewood Cliffs, N. J.: Prentice-Hall, Inc., 1954.

Friedlander, G., and J. Kennedy, *Nuclear and Radiochemistry.* New York: John Wiley & Sons, Inc., 1955, Chapters 7 and 8.

Halliday, D., *Introduction to Nuclear Physics.* New York: John Wiley & Sons, Inc., 1955, Chapters 7 and 8.

Price, William J., *Nuclear Radiation Detection.* New York: McGraw-Hill Book Co., Inc., 1958.

Segre, E. (ed.), *Experimental Nuclear Physics.* New York: John Wiley & Sons, Inc., Vols. I (1953), II (1953), III (1959).

Van Duuren, K., A. J. M. Jasper, and J. Hermsen, "G-M Counters," *Nucleonics,* **17,** 86 (June, 1959).

IV

Sample Preparation and Statistics of Counting

Sample Preparation

In the process of performing many of the experiments in this book, it will be necessary to prepare the final radioactive sample in some suitable fashion for reliable, quantitative counting measurements. In Chapter V the techniques of reproducible counting are considered; in later experiments some of the standard sample preparation methods will be used, among which will be electroplating and filtration. Volatilization in a vacuum from a hot filament is an excellent technique for preparing thin, uniform samples but because of the equipment required is not included in this text.

Evaporation of a solution directly on a counting planchet is one of the simplest methods of sample preparation. Since, with the exception of the counting of gamma rays, it is desirable to minimize the amount of solids in a sample, the radioactivity usually is separated chemically from as much non-isotopic matter as possible. Then, in a minimum volume, the activity is transferred to the counting planchet. For flat plates, the volume can be rarely larger than 0.5 ml. Aluminum, copper, stainless steel and platinum planchets are available with and without a thin ($\frac{1}{8}$ inch) rim. For slightly

larger volumes, stainless steel cups or 25 mm watch glasses may be used. The latter have the advantage of being inexpensive and, also, easy to decontaminate if it is necessary to reuse counting planchets. In case of reuse, each planchet should be carefully checked for residual activity.

Counting samples of dilute or carrier free solutions may be prepared by this method. For small precipitates, it is feasible to dissolve them, then transfer the solution to a planchet and evaporate. The usual practice is to perform the evaporation under an infrared heat lamp. If the solution is raised to its boiling point, spattering occurs, contaminating the area surrounding the planchet. To avoid this, the distance between the heat lamp and the sample must be sufficient to prevent boiling—perhaps, 4 to 8 inches. Also, it should be recognized that volatile samples can not be prepared this way. Even though the radioactive species may not be volatile itself, it may be carried off in significant amounts if a volatile compound is present during the evaporation. Ammonium chloride is to be avoided in sample preparation by evaporation because of the tendency of carrier free activities to be lost with the NH_4Cl "smoke." To ensure a more uniform and evenly spread sample, a small amount of an agent which lowers the surface tension such as tetra-ethylene glycol (TEG) may be added to the aliquot before evaporation. After drying, the planchet should be centered on a counting plate holder if it is used for Geiger-Müller or thin-window proportional counting and covered with thin cellophane or plastic film to prevent spilling. The edges of the film may be secured to the plate holder with Scotch tape. The plate holder may be either aluminum or stiff cardboard of a proper size to fit into the shelf slots of the counting sample holder.

Since sample preparation requires small volumes, micropipets of capacities ranging from 1 microliter ($1\mu l$) to 1000 microliters will be in frequent use in a radiochemical laboratory. It is expedient, then, to be able to use these small capacity pipets in quantitative transfers of solution volumes. The fraction of the total volume that wets the wall in these pipets is much greater than in a macropipet and in discharging the micropipet, the fraction remaining will be significant and will be a function to some extent of the particular solution pipetted. As a consequence, micropipets are calibrated to contain, rather than to deliver, and it is necessary to rinse the pipet sufficiently to achieve quantitative removal. Of course, the pipet must be as clean as possible before use. A setup for pipet washing (Figure 1) can consist of an ordinary glass funnel placed on a suction flask connected to a water aspirator. The less fragile end of the pipet is placed in the neck of funnel and dichromate cleaning solution (or aqua regia or strong acid) dropped on the other tip. The suction will pull the solution through the pipet after which it may be rinsed with distilled water and alcohol or acetone. It will dry in a short time if left under suction after the acetone rinse.

The solution is drawn into the pipet by means of a pipet control. Screw type pipet holders providing very good control are available; however, with a small amount of practice it is possible to use ordinary medical hypodermic syringes. The plunger should be well greased for easy movement and a short piece of plastic or a No. 00 one-hole rubber stopper attached to the bottom of the barrel to hold the pipet. In drawing the solution into the pipet, care should be taken to exceed the calibration mark by only a minimal amount. The pipet is then withdrawn from the solution, the outside wiped dry with an absorbent tissue, such as Kleenex, and the end of the pipet touched lightly with the tissue to draw off the excess above the calibration mark. The technique of this last step should be mastered before any actual work is done with a micropipet. The aliquot is discharged onto a counting planchet by slowly depressing the plunger, keeping the tip of the pipet just in contact with the liquid surface. Be careful as the pipet is emptied not to blow bubbles out as this may spray activity. The pipet tip may be coated with an organo-silicon compound,[1] which minimizes wetting. Rinsings are accomplished in identical fashion. It is helpful to have several extra planchets at hand so that a few drops of the rinsing solution may be placed on these beforehand for ready accessibility during the actual sampling. Of course, these drops should not be used as rinse solution for more than one sample as the first use may contaminate the remaining solution. Water should not be used as a rinsing solvent if there is a possibility of hydrolysis of the residual activity or adsorption on the glass walls. In these cases, use hydrochloric or nitric acid of sufficient concentration to avoid hydrolysis.

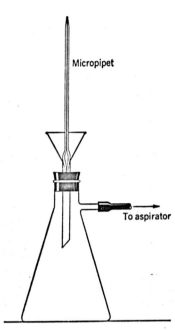

Micropipet

To aspirator

Figure 1. Micropipet cleaning system.

Statistics of Counting

Unless the experimenter has a fair notion of the error limits of any scientific measurement, the answer will be of little use. For example, it serves no purpose to perform an experiment to investigate two systems with an expected difference of 5% if the measured values are uncertain to

[1]"Desicote," Beckman Instruments, Inc.

25%. Two kinds of error will be present: determinate error, which is usually systematic, and constant, and random error, which is neither constant nor systematic. To a large extent, the causes of the former type can be eliminated after the sources of the error are discovered; this is usually done by better design of the experiment. The latter type, however, can not be eliminated but can be evaluated by statistical methods. Assuming a perfectly designed and executed experiment is carried out to measure the count rate of a sample, there will still exist a certain random error because radioactive decay is a random process. Each atom has a certain probability of decay within any one time interval; consequently, since this probability allows unlikely processes to occur occasionally and likely processes not to occur in any particular time interval, the number of decays may be more or less than the number in another similar interval. It is necessary, then, when counting a sample to be able to calculate the probability that the recorded count rate is within certain limits of the true or average count rate. The Binomial Distribution Law correctly expresses this probability but it is common practice to use either the Poisson Distribution or the normal Gaussian Distribution Functions as both approximate the first but are much simpler to use.

Table of Notation

$\bar{n}$ = arithmetic mean of all the measured values
n = a measured value of total counts
$P(n)$ = probability of occurrence of the value n
σ = standard deviation
p = probable error
R = count rate in counts per minute
t = time of measurement

K = number of standard deviations = $\dfrac{|\bar{n} - n|}{\sigma}$

Subscripts

s = sample only
b = background
t = total (sample + background)

The Poisson Distribution equation is

$$P(n) = \frac{\bar{n}^{+n}e^{-\bar{n}}}{n!}$$ (IV-1)

The Poisson Distribution is not symmetric about $\bar{n}$, the average value, for low values of $\bar{n}$ (Figure 2). The Gaussian Distribution is symmetric about his value so that the average value is also the most probable value. If the average number of counts is high (above 100), the Gaussian function may be substituted for the Poisson Distribution with no appreciable error. The probability of observing the value n is then

$$P(n) = \frac{1}{\sqrt{2\pi n}} e^{-\frac{(\bar{n} - n)^2}{2\bar{n}}} \qquad (\text{IV-2})$$

The standard deviation is expressed by

$$\sigma = \sqrt{\frac{1}{N} \sum_{i=1}^{N} (\bar{n} - n_i)^2} = \sqrt{n} \qquad (\text{IV-3})$$

If the error in the rate R rather than in the total number of counts is desired, then

$$\sigma_R = \frac{\sqrt{n}}{t} \qquad (\text{IV-4})$$

The probable error expresses the limits within which there is a 50% probability of the true value occurring.

$$p = 0.67\sigma = 0.67\sqrt{n} \qquad (\text{IV-5})$$

Since σ is so easy to calculate, it is used most frequently to express the error of a measurement. However, it is helpful to know the probability of errors greater or smaller than σ occurring, or how such a probability decreases as K, the number of standard deviations, increases. Figure 3 is a plot of the probability of an error greater than K as a function of K. For example, if a sample has a true count rate of 10,000 cpm, there is a 90% probability $(K = 1.65)$ that a one minute count will fall within the limits 10,000 ± 165 cpm. Such calculations make it possible to establish a rule of thumb for rejection of unlikely data. If any measurement differs from the average value by more than five times the probable error it may be rejected, as the probability is less than 1 in a 1000 that this is a true random error.

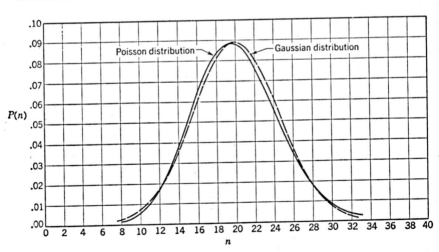

Figure 2. The Poisson and Gaussian distributions for $\bar{n} = 20$.

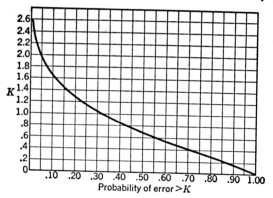

Figure 3

Since a real count is a summation of the sample and the background counts, it is necessary to have expressions for calculation of the errors of sums and differences. The standard deviation for the sample alone will be

$$\sigma_s = (\sigma_t^2 + \sigma_b^2)^{1/2} \tag{IV-6}$$

Usually the background can be counted for a sufficiently long period to make $\sigma_b \ll \sigma_t$. It is practical to perform long background counts while the experiment is in progress. However, if only a limited amount of time is available to determine both sample and background, the optimum ratio of counting times to minimize the net error may be calculated using Equation (IV-7).

$$\frac{t_b}{t_t} = \left(\frac{R_b}{R_t}\right)^{1/2} \tag{IV-7}$$

The error involved in computing dead time corrections is usually not important as the count rates needing these corrections are so high, and the errors are correspondingly small. The error for short counting times is given by Equation (IV-8).

$$\sigma_m = n^{1/2}\left(\frac{m}{n}\right), \qquad m = \text{true count rate} \tag{IV-8}$$

Frequently occasions arise where the experimenter is faced with the problem of choosing between several alternate ways of counting a sample. It may be possible to count gamma rays with a crystal scintillation counter or beta rays with a Geiger-Müller, a proportional, or a scintillation counter. One system may have the advantage of greater sensitivity; however, if it does, it usually has the disadvantage of a higher background. Thus, it is of interest to know which system will require the shorter counting time for the same error. For this equality in error, the ratio in counting times is expressed by

$$\frac{t}{t'} = \frac{\left[\dfrac{(aR_t)^{1/2} + R_b^{1/2}}{R_s}\right]^2}{\left[\dfrac{(aR_t')^{1/2} + R_b'^{1/2}}{R_s'}\right]^2}$$

where a = number of samples,
$\quad R_s = R_t - R_b$ = cpm of sample in first counter,
$\quad t$ = time for first system.
(Prime values are for second system.)

There may occur error during a count not due to the random nature of radioactivity. Such error may be due to electronic or mechanical misbehavior and may cause a decrease or an increase in the count rate. There are two simple tests to check the operational behavior of a system. First, the sample may be counted twice, and the difference, $|n_2 - n_1|$, may be divided by the standard deviation to obtain the value of K. Figure 2 may be used to ascertain the probability that this is a true statistical error or not. The rule of thumb that $K > 3.5$ is indicative of non-statistical behavior may be applied here.

The alternative method of checking the counters for proper operation is known as the Chi-square test. This quantity is defined in Equation (IV-10) for S counting intervals.

$$\chi^2 = \frac{1}{n} \sum_{i=1}^{S} (n_i - \bar{n})^2 \qquad \text{(IV-10)}$$

If 20 counts are taken, values of χ^2 between 11.7 and 27.2 should occur 80% of the time for a random process. However, values less than 10.1 or greater than 30.1 indicate the errors are not purely statistical as the probability of these values being exceeded is only 1 in 20.

Experimental

It is recommended that Experiment 10 (Chapter VI) be begun as soon after Experiment 4 as possible. Micropipets are supplied by a number of industrial concerns (for instance, Corning Glass Works). Directions for making and calibrating micropipets are to be found in these references: A. A. Benedetti-Pichler, *Introduction to Microtechnique of Inorganic Analysis* (New York: John Wiley & Sons Inc., 1942), p. 238; and R. C. Sisco, B. B. Cunningham, and P. L. Kirk, *J. Biol. Chem.*, 139, 1 (1941).

EXPERIMENT 4

Sample Preparation

Purpose:

To study a simple method of sample preparation and to become familiar with handling micropipets.

Method:

Obtain a micropipet of 10–20 microliter (μl) capacity, a syringe control and glass or stainless steel counting planchets. Add stopcock grease to the control until it handles easily. Fit the end of the control with a one hole No. 00 rubber stopper which will hold the pipet firmly.

(1) Practice drawing water up into the pipet, avoiding going over the calibration mark any more than necessary. Dry the pipet tip with a tissue before discharging the solution.

(2) Micropipets are calibrated to contain. After sufficient practice, carefully fill the pipet to the mark from the stock tracer solution, dry the tip and discharge the solution into one drop of 1 M HCl in a glass counting disc. From a second disc containing several drops of HCl, refill the pipet to the mark and repeat the discharge into a fresh disc containing a drop of HCl. Repeat the rinse procedure with another counting disc. Evaporate to dryness the original and the two rinse discs under a heat lamp. Count the three discs for three minutes to determine the number of rinses needed. Do this for both Cs^{137} and Pm^{147}.

(3) With this information, prepare five counting samples as similarly as possible and after drying, count them for 5 minutes each. Their count rates should be between 1000 cpm and 5000 cpm.

Data:

Calculate the percentage of the activity in each of the rinses. Also, determine the standard deviation of the count rate and discuss the possible sources of error in this experiment.

EXPERIMENT 5

Counting Statistics

Purpose:

To study the statistics of counting of radioactivity.

Method:

With one of the samples prepared in the previous experiment, take 30 one-minute counts in succession; also, take a background count for ten minutes. Calculate (1) the average count rate (after subtraction of background); (2) the standard deviation of the average count rate as though it were a 30 minute count; and (3) the standard deviation of each individual one minute count. Also, calculate the standard deviation of the average count rate as if it were only a one minute count. Compare the percentage of the number of individual counts with values outside of the limits of this last standard deviation with the expected 31.7% (see Figure 3, $K = 1$).

Also calculate the probable error for the average count rate as if it were a one minute count and compare the percentage of the number of counts outside of these limits with the expected 50% value.

Be sure to use resolving time corrections for high count rates if a Geiger-Müller counter is used.

PROBLEMS

1. A sample counted for 15 minutes gave 9000 total counts. A 30 minute background count registered 1200 counts. Calculate the count rate of the sample alone with its standard deviation; with its probable error.

2. Four two-minute counts of a sample gave 2130, 2108, 2117, 2132. Express the average count rate with its standard deviation.

3. If only 30 minutes of counting time are available, calculate the desirable division of time between sample and background for minimum error if the background is approximately 30 cpm and the total rate 100 cpm. What will the standard deviation for the sample be, expressed as a percentage error?

4. For a series of 100 counts, n is 100 cpm. How many of the determinations will give 75 cpm, 150 cpm, 100 cpm?

5. In a Geiger-Müller counter, a sample registered a total of 60 cpm with a background of 30 cpm. In a proportional counter the same sample gave 95 cpm with a background of 60 cpm. If 3 such samples are to be counted, which system will give the same error in less time?

6. The following counting data were collected per minute with one sample: 3308, 3277, 3411, 3080, 3580, 3425, 3207, 3436, 3328, 3363 counts. Should any of these counts be rejected if it is desired to calculate a good average count rate?

7. A Geiger-Müller counter has a background of 18 cpm with a lead shield. Unshielded, the background rises to 48 cpm. For a sample which counts 60 cpm above background, what are the necessary counting times in the shielded and unshielded arrangements to obtain 5% probable error?

8. The same sample is counted with two different Geiger-Müller counters to determine whether their absolute sensitivity is the same. Counter 1 gave 500 counts in the same time interval that Counter 2 gave 525 counts. Is this a statistically significant difference? Would the difference be significant if the two counts were 500 and 590?

9. Calculate the total number of counts that must be collected in each case for a count rate of 500 cpm to give probable errors of 0.1%, 0.5%, 1%, 5%, 10%, 50%.

10. Two successive counts in a proportional counter of the same sample for the same interval gave values of 5440 and 5600. Can the counter be considered to be operating normally? What would be the most probable conclusion if the two counts were 5440 and 5750?

REFERENCES

Bleuler, E., and G. J. Goldsmith, *Experimental Nucleonics.* New York: Rinehart & Co., Inc., 1952.

Evans, R. D., *The Atomic Nucleus.* New York: McGraw-Hill Book Co., Inc., 1955, Chapters 26–28.

Kirk, P. L., *Quantitative Ultramicroanalysis.* New York: John Wiley & Sons, Inc., 1950, Chapter 2.

Kuyper, Adrian C., "The Statistics of Radioactivity Measurements," *J. Chem. Educ.*, **36**, 128 (1959).

Margenau, H., and G. M. Murphy, *The Mathematics of Physics and Chemistry.* New York: D. Van Nostrand Co., 1943, Chapter 13.

Price, W. J., *Nuclear Radiation Detection.* New York: McGraw-Hill Book Co., Inc., 1958, Chapter 3.

Steinberg, E. P., *U. S. A. E. C. Rept. ANL-5622.* Washington, D. C.: Office of Technical Services, Department of Commerce, 1956.

V

Absolute Disintegration Rates
and Absorption Measurements

MANY situations arise in using radioisotopes when it is desirable or even
necessary to ascertain the true disintegration rate of a sample and not
some relative count rate. For example, if the reaction probability (the
cross section) is to be determined following a cyclotron irradiation, the
absolute disintegration rate must be obtained so that the number of product nuclei may be calculated. The determination of such a true disintegration rate from a measured count rate is more difficult, in general, for
beta emitting nuclides than for alpha or gamma emitters. Comparison
with a standard of known disintegration rate, prepared and counted in a
similar fashion to the unknown, is the simplest technique. Such standards
are available commercially for beta emitters over a wide range of energies.
Another satisfactory method is 4π beta counting, which is a technique
whereby the sample is mounted on a very thin support and placed in the
center of a windowless flow counting chamber so that particles emitted in
any direction pass into a sensitive part of the counter and are recorded.

This method provides the most accurate absolute beta activity measurements at the present time.[1]

In cases where standards or 4π counters are not available, ordinary Geiger-Müller counting may be performed and the approximate disintegration rate calculated from a knowledge of the various counting factors. The detection efficiency C is defined as the ratio between the measured count rate and the absolute disintegration rate.

$$C = \frac{A\,(\text{dpm})}{m\,(\text{cpm})} \qquad \text{(V-1)}$$

This detection efficiency is a product of all the factors which influence the measured count rate and may be expressed by

$$C = f_e \cdot f_\gamma \cdot f_g \cdot f_b \cdot f_s \cdot f_a \qquad \text{(V-2)}$$

where f_e = counting efficiency of tube,
f_γ = resolving time correction,
f_g = geometry factor,
f_b = backscattering factor,
f_s = self-absorption factor,
f_a = absorption factor.

The counting efficiency in the Geiger-Müller tube is a measure of the number of counts registered compared to the number of particles entering the sensitive volume of the tube. Since the production of even a single ion pair is sufficient to initiate a discharge, f_e will have a value of unity for a good Geiger-Müller tube. The effect of multiple discharges due to failure of the quencher is included in f_e but will be negligible for a good tube operating at the proper plateau voltage.

The resolving time correction factor, f_γ, has been discussed, and the method of its evaluation described in Chapter III.

From simple geometric considerations of the solid angle subtended by the tube window it is possible to derive the expression for the geometry factor, f_g, for a point source. This relationship is

$$f_g = 0.5\left[1 - \frac{d}{(d^2 + r^2)^{1/2}}\right] \qquad \text{(V-3)}$$

In this expression r is the inside radius of the tube (in general r is the window diameter for end window tubes) while d is the distance between the source and the sensitive volume of the tube. This is not exactly the same as the distance from the source to window itself as charge collection on the window renders a small volume inside the tube insensitive. A good approximation of the width of this insensitive volume is 4 mm; consequently d is the source to window distance plus 4 mm. Since this expression is derived for a point source and most real samples cover a significant area (1 − 2

[1] H. H. Seliger, and A. Schwebel, *Nucleonics* **12**, 54 (July 1954).

cm^2), the smaller the distance between source and tube, the less valid is the equation. Frequently Geiger-Müller windows are slightly curved which introduces an additional complication in the exact calculation of f_g. In actual practice, it is better to evaluate the combined effects of f_s and f_g experimentally by using a very thin, standard source spread over approximately the same area as the unknown. The use of Equation (V-3) in the absence of standard sources permits calculation of f_g to within 10% of the true value in most cases. Some windowless proportional flow counters have 2π geometry, so their f_g is very close to 0.5.

In the discussion in Chapter III, the case with which beta rays undergo large angle deflections was mentioned. As a result of the relatively high probability for such events, a significant number of beta rays which start out in the direction away from the tube may be deflected back into the tube after multiple scattering. This scattering may be caused by the sample itself if it is thick enough or by the backing material upon which it is mounted. The backscattering factor, f_b, will have a value between 1 and 2 and is the ratio between the count rate of the sample as prepared on the backing material and that of the same amount of sample suspended freely in a vacuum. Scattering will occur also from the walls of the holder but, especially if the holder is constructed of a low Z material, such as aluminum or lucite, this will be much less important than backscattering. Backscattering will be appreciable from the floor of the holder for a thin sample if the lowest shelves are used for counting.

The higher the atomic number of the scattering material, the larger is f_b. Also, f_b increases with thickness up to a saturation thickness beyond which it is a constant. Counting is done usually with essentially weightless backing ($f_b = 1$) or with a thick enough backing to have saturation. It might be expected that the saturation thickness would be one half of the range of the beta particles in the backing material as this thickness must be traveled twice before detection. Actually, it is close to 20% of the range which is understandable when it is realized that approximately 95% of the beta particles are stopped in the first half of the total range.

Since the scattered beta particles suffer degradation of energy in scattering, this will be a more important correction for windowless or thin window counters, as all the low energy scattered electrons will be counted in these. Experimentally, f_b may seem to be a function of beta energy; however, if a correction is made for the loss of low energy back scattered particles by absorption in the air above the sample and the counting tube window, f_b is independent of beta energy (Figure 1).

If the sample is thick, the count rate may be increased by internal backscattering, but it may also be decreased by self-absorption. This sample self-absorption will be greater the lower the beta energy and the thicker the sample. For P^{32} (1.72 Mev) sample thicknesses of 15 mg/cm^2 show little absorption while C^{14} (0.15 Mev) has significant absorption for

1 mg/cm². For a given specific activity (dpm per mg of sample), the count rate decreases with increased thickness until a minimum constant rate is obtained. The absorption factor may be measured by counting a series of samples of different thickness with the same total count rate, then extrapolating back to zero sample weight.

The absorption of beta particles has an exponential dependence on the absorber thickness.

$$I = I_0 e^{-\mu d} \qquad\qquad (V\text{-}4)$$

where I = intensity after thickness d,
  I_0 = initial intensity,
  μ = absorber coefficient,
  d = thickness of absorber.

For a source of uniform thickness, the relationship between f_s, the self-absorption factor, and μ, the absorption coefficient, is expressed in cm² per mg by

$$f_s = \frac{1}{\mu S} (1 - e^{-\mu S}) \qquad\qquad (V\text{-}5)$$

for a sample thickness of S mg per cm². For beta energies between 0.5 and 6 Mev, it is possible to estimate μ from the maximum beta energy in Mev by use of Equation (V-6).

$$\mu = \frac{22}{E^{1.33}} \qquad\qquad (V\text{-}6)$$

The absorption factor, f_a, takes into account the absorption and scattering of beta particles by the sample covering and the tube window, and, in addition, by the air between these two. The losses in tube windows of

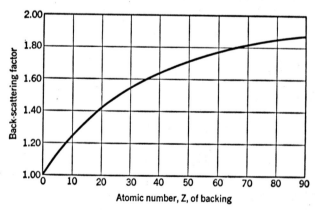

Figure 1. Corrected saturation back-scattering factor (f_b) as a function of the atomic number of the scatterer. [L. R. Zumwalt, *Document AECU-567*, AEC (1950).]

different thicknesses is shown in Figure 2 as a function of beta energy. The air thickness in centimeters may be multiplied by a factor of 1.18 to obtain the equivalent thickness in mg per cm^2. This may be added to the tube window thickness (also in mg per cm^2) to get a total thickness of absorber. It is customary to obtain f_a by counting the sample with various thicknesses of aluminum absorber interposed between the sample and the tube, then extrapolating the count rate curve back from zero aluminum absorber through the thickness in mg per cm^2 of the air-window to zero total absorber. The quantity f_a is the ratio between the count rate for zero aluminum absorber and the extrapolated count rate for zero total absorber.

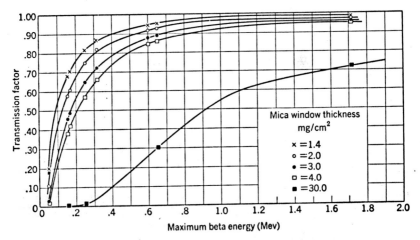

Figure 2. Transmission factor as a function of beta energy. (*Technical Bulletin No. 2*, Nucleonic Corporation of America)

This extrapolation process becomes difficult if the beta energy is small as the aluminum absorber curve will have a good deal of curvature. Also, a "tail" due to gamma and X rays will be observed as the beta particles are removed by thicker absorbers. Since scattering will occur in the aluminum absorber, it is recommended that the absorber be placed as close to the detector window as possible.

Other variables influence the measured count rate of a sample, such as the exact position on the shelf in relation to the window. Care in reproducing as exactly as possible the conditions for preparing and counting the sample can make these variables unimportant. Bayhurst and Prestwood have reported a method for estimating beta-counting efficiencies to within 3% which eliminates the necessity for making separate corrections for f_a, f_s, etc.[2]

[2] B. P. Bayhurst, and R. J. Prestwood, *Nucleonics*, 17, 82 (March 1959).

Maximum Beta Energy

From the same absorber measurements used to obtain f_a it is possible to calculate the maximum beta energy. Since the loss of energy by radiation (*bremsstrahlung*) is proportional to the atomic number of the absorber, low Z materials are used in order that energy loss by ionization be favored. This results in a single mode of energy loss and, hence, a simpler absorption curve. Aluminum is the normal absorber although beryllium is also used. The toxicity of beryllium reduces its attractiveness to the experimenter. The range of beta particles in aluminum as a function of the maximum beta energy is shown in Figure 3. It has been mentioned that 95% of the electrons are stopped in the first half of the range. Consequently, the thickness necessary to stop 50% of the particles (Figure 4) is frequently of greater value experimentally due to the difficulty of measuring precisely the total range since very few electrons have the full end-point energy.

It is possible to calculate the range to a good approximation from the empirical equations of Glendenin[3] where R is the range in aluminum in mg per cm^2 and E is the beta energy in Mev.

$$R = 542E - 133 \qquad 0.8 < E < 3 \text{ Mev}$$
$$R = 407E^{1.38} \qquad 0.15 < E < 0.8 \text{ Mev} \qquad \text{(V-7)}$$

If the energy and range are both unknown, the relationship

$$I_d = (R - d)^4 \qquad \text{(V-8)}$$

may be used to obtain the range. The fourth root of the intensity, $I_d^{1/4}$, is plotted on a linear scale as a function of the absorber thickness d in mg per cm^2. The resulting straight line is extrapolated to $I_d^{1/4} = 0$ to get the value for R, the range. This value may be substituted in Equation (V-7) to calculate the maximum beta energy.

The method capable of the greatest accuracy for determination of maximum beta end-point energies from absorber measurements is the Feather analysis. The absorption curve of the sample after subtraction of all gamma- and X-ray background is compared to that of some standard beta emitter such as P^{32}. The assumption is made that the same fraction of the initial intensity will be removed by equal fractions of the total range. For example, if the P^{32} activity is reduced to 25% of its initial intensity in the first one fourth of the range, then for a second beta emitter, the thickness necessary to reduce the intensity to 25% represents a quarter of the total range. Since the shapes of the beta spectra are different, different values of the total range will be obtained and extrapolation of a graph of apparent range versus the fraction of the range gives the final value. The

[3] L. E. Glendenin, *Nucleonics*, **2**, 12 (January 1948).

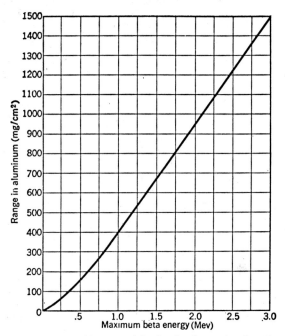

Figure 3. Range of beta particles in aluminum as a function of beta energy.

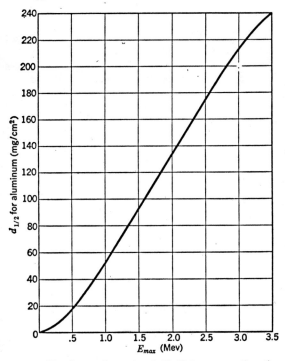

Figure 4. Aluminum absorption half-thickness as a function of beta-ray energy.

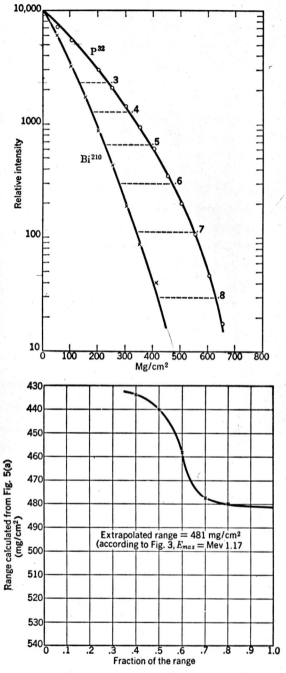

Figure 5. (a) Aluminum absorber curves—horizontal lines connect points of equal fractions of the total range. (b) Extrapolation of calculated range of Bi²¹⁰ beta rays to obtain true range.

range of P^{32} is taken as 780 mg per cm^2 in aluminum for this analysis. Figures 5a and 5b present Feather analysis plots for Bi^{210}. The extrapolated range is used with Figure 3 or Equation (V-7) to calculate the maximum beta energy.

Knowledge of the maximum beta energy is useful in identifying unknown activities, in determining decay schemes and in absolute beta counting. The methods of this chapter for beta-energy evaluation are useful approximations but for precise measurements, it is necessary to use magnetic beta-ray spectrometers. It is also possible to use a scintillation spectrometer with an organic crystal detector to obtain beta energies (Chapter VII).

Gamma-Ray Absorption

An exponential absorption Equation (V-8) is valid for gamma rays, where

$$I = I_0 e^{-\mu d} \tag{V-8}$$

The absorption coefficient, μ, is a summation of the absorption coefficients for the photoelectric effect, the Compton effect and pair production (see Chapter III). Since an individual gamma ray is removed from the beam in a single event, it is not possible to assign a definite range for gamma rays. Instead of a range, it is more proper to speak of the probability that a gamma ray will not travel farther than some definite distance. A plot of log I versus thickness of absorber should produce a straight line if gamma rays of only one energy are emitted. If several different energy gamma rays are present, each energy will be represented by a straight line of slope equal to $-\mu/2.3$ where μ is the absorption coefficient for that energy. It is necessary to resolve the total observed absorption curve into its straight line components if any useful information on a gamma ray of one energy is to be gained. Usually, it is not possible to resolve curves of more than three components and even for three the energies must not be too similar.

Consider the situation when the intensity has been reduced to 50% of its original value; then

$$\ln \frac{I_0}{I} = \ln 2 = \mu d_{1/2}$$

$$\therefore \quad \mu = \frac{0.693}{d_{1/2}} \tag{V-9}$$

The absorber thickness necessary to reduce the original intensity by 50% (the $d_{1/2}$ value) is inversely proportional to the absorption coefficient. Since gamma rays are so penetrating, absorber measurements are made with dense, high Z elements to reduce the thickness necessary to obtain a definite reduction in intensity. Whereas aluminum is used for beta rays and may be used for gamma rays, it is preferable to use lead for the latter.

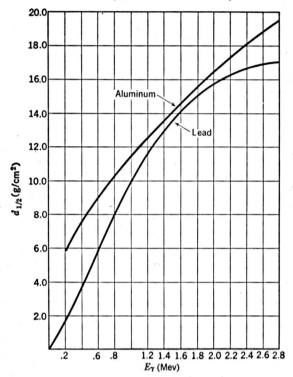

Figure 6. Absorption half-thickness curves for aluminum and lead as a function of gamma-ray energy.

With the aid of curves such as those of Figure 6, it is possible to obtain fairly good values of gamma ray energies.

The geometric considerations for beta rays will be true for gamma rays also. However, the much greater penetrating power of the gamma rays make sample self-absorption, the air + window absorption and back-scattering much less important. The intrinsic efficiency for Geiger-Müller counters is much less for gamma rays ($\sim1\%$) than for beta rays ($\sim100\%$). Higher counting efficiencies and more precise energy determinations are obtainable by use of solid crystal scintillation detection, which will be discussed in Chapter VII. The error in the method of gamma ray energy determination by absorber measurements is due in large part to scattering by the sample holder stand which will reflect gamma rays into the sensitive volume of the counting tube without the necessity of passage through the absorber.

A nomogram, such as that shown in Figure 7, is useful in calculating absorption of gamma rays. If the reduction of the intensity is measured with one lead absorber of known thickness, the intersection on the $d_{1/2}$

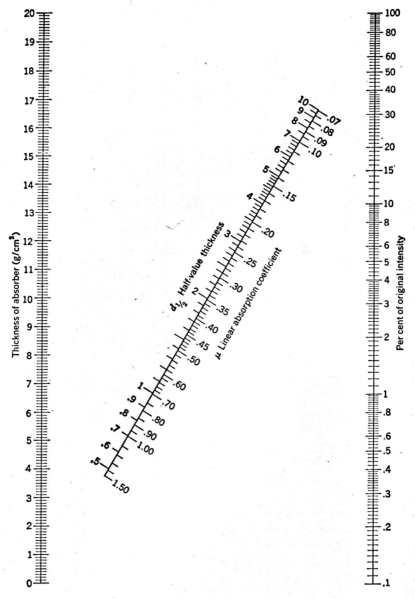

Figure 7. Nomogram for absorption of mono-energetic X rays and gamma rays by lead. [M. H. Green, "Data Sheet No. 34," *Nucleonics*, **17**, 77 (October, 1959)]

scale of a straight line connecting the first two values gives the value of $d_{1/2}$ which may in turn be used with Figure 6 to estimate E. The reverse process of calculating the thickness of lead absorber necessary to reduce a gamma ray of known energy to some lower intensity may be done also with the aid of Figure 7. This nomogram can be used only for nuclides which emit a single gamma ray or for those which emit more than one gamma ray, where the intensity for one gamma ray is much greater than for the others.

Experimental

All the following experiments are to be done with an end window Geiger counter. It is rather easy to scratch or break the thin window in inserting or removing the absorbers since they should be placed on the uppermost possible shelf. Care should be taken in these manipulations. In handling the samples, no possibility of contamination of the sample holder stand or

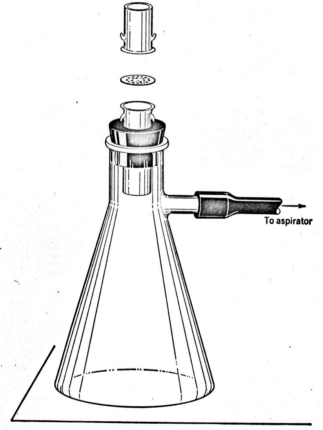

Figure 8. Filter assembly for obtaining uniform deposits.

the tube should be allowed. The sample holders may be aluminum or stiff cardboard rectangles with a one half to an inch diameter hole in the center. In Experiment 6 the sample is counted on the top shelf to minimize backscattering from the floor of the sample holder stand.

In Experiment 8 be careful to include resolving time corrections if the count rates are sufficiently high.

In Experiment 7 the sample is prepared by precipitation and filtration. Since there is no stable isotope of promethium, lanthanum, which possesses very similar chemical properties to promethium, is used to carry down the trace promethium by the process of coprecipitation. The filter assembly is shown in Figure 8. The glass chimneys may be made from 2 cm I.D. glass tubing by thickening the ends in a flame and then grinding them to a flush fit with the filter plate. It is recommended that the latter be of sintered glass, firepolished on the rim, but a multihole plate will serve if the filtration is performed sufficiently slowly to obtain an even deposit. Glass fiber filter papers[4] are to be preferred but satisfactory results are obtainable with circles punched out of ordinary filter paper.

EXPERIMENT 6

Scattering

Purpose:

To study the effect of scattering on the measured count rate.

Method:

(1) Prepare a counting sample as follows. Cut a piece of cellophane to fit over the hole in a sample holder. Scotch tape it in place on the bottom of the holder. With a micropipet, transfer approximately 4000 cpm (Shelf 1—Geiger-Müller) of Pm^{147} from the stock tracer solution to the cellophane and carefully evaporate to dryness under an infrared lamp. Cut another piece of cellophane, Scotch tape it over the sample and mark it "top." Repeat this process for Tl^{204}. Take care in handling these samples that no solid material is displaced.

(2) Count the samples as prepared for 5 minutes on the top shelf of the holder. Repeat the 5 minute count with squares of plastic, aluminum, copper, and lead (at least 250 mg per cm^2 thick to ensure saturation) carefully taped to the back of the sample holder. Plot the net count minus background versus Z, the atomic number, of the scatterer.

(3) Count the sample with aluminum absorbers, increasing the thick-

[4] Scientific Glass Apparatus Co., Inc., Bloomfield, N. J.

ness of the absorber after each count. Continue until no further change in count rate is observed with additional aluminum. Plot cpm versus d, the thickness in mg per cm².

(4) Determine the atomic number of an unknown material by using it in a backscattering experiment.

Caution:

(1) Be careful not to contaminate absorbers!

(2) Be careful not to break or scratch tube window.

EXPERIMENT 7

Sample Self-absorption

Purpose:

To study the effect on count rate of sample thickness.

Method:

Prepare in 0.5 M HNO₃ 1 ml of La(NO₃)₃ solutions containing 7.5, 15.0, 22.5, 30.0, 37.4, 45.0, and 75 mg of La(III). This may be conveniently done by preparing a solution of 150 mg per ml of La(III) and another of 1 M HNO₃ and adding the proper aliquot before dilution to 1 ml (see below). The exact amounts of La(III) are important but not the exact solution concentrations. Add the same amount of Pm¹⁴⁷ tracer (approximately 10,000 cpm) to each of the tubes and at the same time prepare a sample of this amount of activity as in Experiment 2. Add 5 ml of saturated ammonium oxalate to each tube and cool for 10 minutes in an ice bath before filtering. Quantitatively transfer the precipitate to a filter assembly and wash each with 2 ml of H₂O, 2 ml of ethanol and 2 ml of acetone.

Filter slowly enough to obtain an even deposit. Air dry, take the filter assembly apart, and carefully dry the filter paper and precipitate under a heat lamp (be careful not to char the paper). After drying, mount the filter paper and precipitate in a sample holder and cover with cellophane on top and bottom as before. (Assume that backscattering from the filter paper is not significant. It may increase the count rate 1–2% for thin samples.) Count each sample for at least 5000 total counts.

Data:

(1) Plot the cpm versus sample weight as La₂(C₂O₄)₃·10 H₂O.

(2) After completion of experiments 3, 6, 7, and 8, estimate the absolute disintegration rate of the Pm¹⁴⁷ sample in this experiment.

$$A(\text{dpm}) = \frac{m}{f_\gamma \cdot f_a \cdot f_b \cdot f_s \cdot f_g}$$

where A = absolution disintegration rate,
m = observed count rate,
f_γ = dead time correction,
f_a = absorber correction between sample and tube,
f_b = backscatter factor,
f_s = sample absorption factor,
f_g = geometry factor.

Weight of La	Aliquot
7.5 mg	50 μl
15.0 mg	100 μl
22.5 mg	150 μl
30.0 mg	200 μl
37.5 mg	250 μl
45.0 mg	300 μl
75.0 mg	500 μl

EXPERIMENT 8

Absorption Curves and Range-energy of Beta Particles

Purpose:

To use absorber measurements to calculate beta ray energies.

Method:

(1) Prepare a source with Pm^{147} on plastic film (or cellophane) as in Experiment 2. A count rate of 10,000 cpm on the third shelf of the Geiger-Müller counting holder is desirable. Collect between 5000 to 10,000 total counts for each aluminum absorber added. Repeat this experiment for similar samples of P^{32}, I^{131} and Cs^{137}. Use enough absorber points to define a good, complete curve (for example, to 750 mg/cm^2 for P^{32}). For all the samples:

(a) Plot the cpm versus absorber thickness on semilog paper using as the zero point no absorber at all. Thus the zero aluminum absorber point will correspond to an absorber thickness due to the counter tube window, the air between the source and the tube and the cellophane covering. Determine the latter by weighing a piece of known area. Be certain to extrapolate back any gamma- or X-ray tail to obtain the pure β absorption curve. Extrapolate back

to obtain cpm with 0 absorber. Calculate f_a, the absorption factor.

(b) Determine the half-thickness values and from this, the beta energy end point using Figure 4.

(c) Using the relation $I_d = (R - d)^4$, plot $I^{1/4}$ versus d on a linear scale and extrapolate the resulting straight line to get the range. Calculate the E_β from Equation (V-7).

(d) Using P^{32} ($E_\beta = 1.71$ Mev), calculate the range of the Pm^{147} from a Feather analysis. Use the range of P^{32} as 780 mg/cm² of Al. Again calculate E_β and compare with the results from (c). Resolve the I^{131} and Cs^{137} curves and determine the E_β of the observed groups.

Caution:

Place absorbers as close to the tube as possible.

EXPERIMENT 9

Gamma Absorption Curves

Purpose:

To use gamma absorption curves to obtain gamma ray energies.

Method:

(1) Use Na^{22}, Co^{60}, and Cs^{137} samples which have counting rates of 5000 to 10,000 cpm after removal of β^- particles and secondary electrons by 1 g per cm² (3mm) of Al. This Al absorber should be placed above the Pb absorbers as close to the tube window as possible. Repeat the absorber measurements, using Pb absorbers. Again, plot log (cpm—background) versus absorber thickness in mg per cm². If a straight line is not obtained, resolve it into its components and determine μ, the total absorption coefficient, for each component as well as the half thickness. Determine the gamma energies from the $d_{1/2}$ values using Figure 6.

(2) Use Figure 7 to estimate the E_γ for Cs^{137} from the experimental absorber thickness necessary to reduce the intensity to approximately 10% of the original value. Compare this value with that obtained from the total absorption curve.

REFERENCES

Bleuler, E., and G. J. Goldsmith, *Experimental Nucleonics*. New York: Rinehart & Co., Inc., 1952.

Duncan, J. F., and F. G. Thomas, *Nucleonics*, 15, No. 10, 82 (1957).

Lapp, R. E., and H. L. Andrews, *Nuclear Radiation Physics.* Englewood Cliffs, N. J.: Prentice-Hall, Inc., 1954, Chapter 15.

Nervik, W. E., and P. C. Stevenson, *Nucleonics,* **10,** No. 3, 18 (1952).

Price, W. J., *Nuclear Radiation Detection.* New York: McGraw-Hill Book Co., Inc., 1958, Chapters 1 and 5.

Steinberg, E. P., *U. S. A. E. C. Rept. ANL-5622.* Washington, D. C.: Office of Technical Services, Department of Commerce, 1956.

VI

Radioactive Growth and Decay

FOR the molecule N_2O_4, dissociation occurs by the reaction

$$N_2O_{4(g)} \longrightarrow 2\,NO_{2(g)}$$

The rate of the dissociative process will be proportional to the concentration of the dissociating component and if the products are removed as formed, this reaction will show first-order reaction kinetics. The case of a radioactive nucleus is completely analogous to this system and so may be treated by the first-order reaction rate equation. The rate of disintegration is $-dN/dt$, where N is the number of active atoms present in the sample. Since

$$-\frac{dN}{dt} \propto N$$

then
$$-\frac{dN}{dt} = \lambda N \tag{VI-1}$$

where λ is the proportionality constant known as the decay constant. It may be shown in a similar fashion that the average time of existence τ of a radioactive atom before decay is the reciprocal of the decay constant.

Since

$$\tau = \frac{1}{\lambda} \qquad \text{(VI-2)}$$

and λ is expressed in units of reciprocal time (sec^{-1}, min^{-1}, yr^{-1}), τ will be in the units of time.

Integration of Equation (VI-1) gives

$$\ln N = -\lambda t + C \qquad \text{(VI-3)}$$

To evaluate C, the integration constant, let N_0 represent the number of atoms at time $t = 0$; then

$$\ln N_0 = C \qquad \text{(VI-4)}$$

$$\ln N = -\lambda t + \ln N_0$$

and

$$N = N_0 e^{-\lambda t} \qquad \text{(VI-5)}$$

If A is used to designate $-dN/dt$, the disintegration rate, Equation (VI-1) becomes

$$A = \lambda N \qquad \text{(VI-6)}$$

and, consequently,

$$A = A_0 e^{-\lambda t} \qquad \text{(VI-7)}$$

These last two equations are of great importance, as the experimental quantity usually measured is not the number of atoms present but rather the activity or some count rate proportional to it. In most actual cases,

$$A \text{(in counts per minute)} = C\lambda N$$

where C is the counting efficiency discussed in the previous chapters.

Consider the time necessary for the disintegration rate to decrease to one half of the original value. At this time (designated as $t_{1/2}$) $A = 0.5\,A_0$, therefore,

$$\frac{A}{A_0} = 0.5 = e^{-\lambda t_{1/2}}$$

$$\lambda t_{1/2} = -\ln 0.5 = \ln 2$$

$$t_{1/2} = \frac{0.683}{\lambda} \qquad \text{(VI-8)}$$

The half life (and, of course, the decay constant) is a definitive characteristic of a radioactive species since it is very unlikely that any two nuclides will have exactly the same half life. Except for a few cases of electron capture decay, the half life is completely unaffected by the previous history or present chemical or physical state of the sample and even in these few exceptions in electron capture, the effect is very small. This makes knowledge of the half life an invaluable asset in many situations in radiochemistry. Positive identification of a nuclide can be made very often from knowledge of the half life and either the decay energies or the probable

atomic number. The observed decrease in intensity may be compared to the known half life to check the radiochemical purity of a sample. For tracer experiments lasting over a period of time sufficient for a measurable decrease in the decay rate, use of Equation (VI-7) after calculation of λ from the half life by Equation (VI-8) makes it possible to compare all counts at the same point in time. Alternately, Figure 1 may be used to

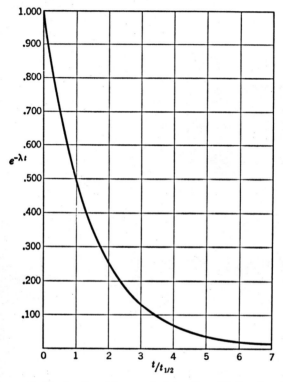

Figure 1. The fractional decrease in intensity, with time in units of the number of half lives.

obtain the fractional decrease during the time t for this correction. Comparison of Equations (VI-4) and (VI-8) demonstrates that the average lifetime τ is about one and a half times as great as the half life.

The half life may be evaluated experimentally by counting a sample over a period of time long enough for the original intensity to be decreased appreciably, preferably enough to include several half life periods. It is necessary to be certain that the counting efficiency either does not change or can be corrected if it does. After subtraction of background, the activity is plotted on semilog paper as a function of time. If only one radioactive species is present, a straight line should result, from which the value of $t_{1/2}$ may be obtained. However, if two activities of different half lives are present in the sample, then a curve such as Figure 2 is obtained. This will be the situation, for example, in samples containing 2 activities which are isotopic with each other and subsequently are not separable chemically. Also, if the decay product is radioactive itself, complex curves will be obtained. To resolve such a curve, the longer lived component should be extrapolated back with a straight line to $t = 0$ (Figure 2, line A).

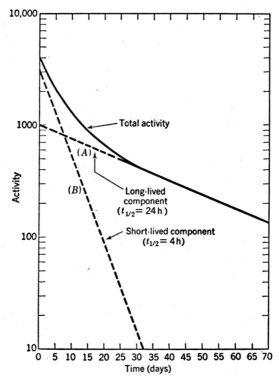

Figure 2. Analysis of a decay curve with two components.

This line is subtracted from the measured curve to obtain the **decay line** for the shorter lived one (Figure 2, line B). If more than two components are present, this procedure of extrapolation and subtraction should be repeated as often as necessary to resolve the curve into straight line components. Because of the uncertainties in the measured activity values, it is not usually possible to resolve curves of more than three components.

If the half life is so short that the period of time of a single counting determination is a significant fraction of the half life, satisfactory results are obtained by plotting the activity at the mid-point of the counting period. For short half lives, this difficulty is overcome by sending the output of the detector to a count rate meter (whose integration time is much

less than the $t_{1/2}$ to be measured) rather than a scalar and recording the meter readings as a continuous curve on a recorder (see Experiment 17, Chapter VIII). It is possible to measure very short half lives by coincidence techniques. In coincidence measurements, only those radiations will be counted by a second detector which occur within a certain very short time after a radiation pulse is counted in the primary detector. By varying this acceptance time, different numbers of coincidences are observed. If the first detector is sensitive to an emission from the decay of a long lived parent and the second to an emission from a very short lived daughter, the net result of the coincidence is to record the number of disintegrations occurring as a function of the time after the decay of the parent. A plot of the logarithm of the number of coincidences versus the acceptance time allows evaluation of the half life of the daughter.

Branching Decay

Some nuclides decay by more than one mode; for example, the isotope of indium with mass number 112 has a state which decays 44% of the time by β^+, 24% by β^- and 32% by electron capture. For many cases of neutron deficient isotopes, positron emission and electron capture will compete with each other. In the heaviest elements, alpha emission and even spontaneous fission may compete with beta emission or electron capture. Each mode of decay in these cases may be treated separately and a decay constant assigned to it. The total decay constant is the sum of these partial constants and the rate of disappearance of the active species is governed by this total constant. For In^{112},

$$\lambda_T = \lambda_{\beta^+} + \lambda_{\beta^-} + \lambda_{E.C.} \qquad (VI-9)$$

and since the measured $t_{1/2}$ is 15 minutes,

$$\lambda_T = \frac{0.693}{15} = 0.0462 \text{ min}^{-1}$$

$$\lambda_{\beta^+} = 0.24 \times 0.0462 = 0.0111 \text{ min}^{-1}$$

$$\lambda_{\beta^-} = 0.44 \times 0.0462 = 0.0203 \text{ min}^{-1}$$

$$\lambda_{E.C.} = 0.32 \times 0.0462 = 0.0148 \text{ min}^{-1}$$

Although the observed decay rate by any mode will be that corresponding to λ_T, it is helpful at times to consider the half life which would be observed if no alternate modes were possible. Thus for In^{112}

$$t_{1/2\beta^+} = \frac{0.693}{0.0111} = 62.4 \text{ min}$$

and in similar manner, values of 34.1 min and 46.8 min are calculated for the partial half lives for the β^- and E.C. processes.

Successive Radioactive Decays

The naturally occurring nuclides between uranium and lead may be grouped into 3 separate families with all the members of each family linked together by a chain of alpha and beta decays. In these families as well as in many other cases throughout the periodic table where a radioactive parent may decay to a daughter species which is also radioactive, it is of interest to be able to calculate the activity of the daughter in association with the parent as a function of time. The net rate of formation of the daughter atoms will be the difference between their rate of formation (equal to the rate of decay of the parent) and their rate of decay; i.e.

$$\frac{dN_2}{dt} = \lambda_1 N_1 - \lambda_2 N_2 \qquad \text{(VI-10a)}$$

where the subscript 1 refers to the parent and 2 to the daughter. The solution of this equation is

$$N_2 = \frac{\lambda_1}{\lambda_2 - \lambda_1} N_1^0 \left(e^{-\lambda_1 t} - e^{-\lambda_2 t}\right) + N_2^0 e^{-\lambda_2 t} \qquad \text{(VI-10b)}$$

when N_1^0 is the number of parent atoms present at time $t = 0$. If the parent is completely purified at time $t = 0$, then the number of atoms of daughter in the parent sample at this time will be zero ($N_2^0 = 0$).

$$\therefore \quad N_2 = \frac{\lambda_1}{\lambda_2 - \lambda_1} N_1^0 \left(e^{-\lambda_1 t} - e^{-\lambda_2 t}\right) \qquad \text{(VI-11)}$$

The 3 situations most often encountered will now be considered by the use of Equation (VI-11).

Case I. $t_{1/2}$ *(parent)* $< t_{1/2}$ *(daughter)*

If the parent is shorter lived than the daughter, the daughter activity will grow to some maximum value, then decay with its own characteristic half life (Figure 3). The time necessary for this maximum daughter intensity to be reached is given by

$$t_m = \frac{2.303}{\lambda_2 - \lambda_1} \log \frac{\lambda_2}{\lambda_1} \qquad \text{(VI-12)}$$

Case II. $t_{1/2}$ *(parent)* $> t_{1/2}$ *(daughter)*

In this case for sufficiently large values of t, Equation (VI-12) reduces to

$$N_2 = \frac{\lambda_1}{\lambda_2 - \lambda_1} N_1^0 e^{-\lambda_1 t} \quad \text{as} \quad e^{-\lambda_1 t} \gg e^{-\lambda_2 t}$$

$$\therefore \quad N_2 = \frac{\lambda_1}{\lambda_2 - \lambda_1} N_1 \qquad \text{(VI-13)}$$

Since $\lambda_1/(\lambda_2 - \lambda_1)$ is a constant, there will be a constant proportionality between N_1, the number of parent atoms, and N_2, the number of daughter

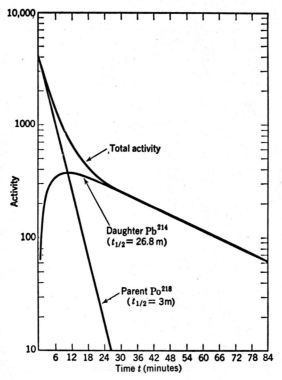

Figure 3. Growth and decay curves for $Po^{218} \rightarrow Pb^{214}$ system.

atoms, for the values of t, which make Equation (VI-13) valid. This condition is known as transient equilibrium even though it is a steady state and not a true equilibrium situation. If Equation (VI-8) is substituted into Equation (VI-13), the result is

$$A_2 = \frac{\lambda_2}{\lambda_2 - \lambda_1} A_1 \qquad \text{(VI-14)}$$

The time necessary to obtain the maximum daughter activity is expressed again by Equation (VI-12).

Case III. $t_{1/2}$ *(parent)* $\gg$ $t_{1/2}$ *(daughter)*

For parent activities whose intensities show no apparent decrease during the period of observation, then $N_1 \approx N_1^0$. Also, as $\lambda_1 \rightarrow 0$, $e^{-\lambda_1 t} \rightarrow 1$ and as in Case II, for sufficiently large values of t, $e^{-\lambda_2 t} \rightarrow 0$; therefore Equation (VI-11) becomes

$$N_2 = \frac{\lambda_1}{\lambda_2} N_1^0 \qquad \text{(VI-15a)}$$

or $$A_2 = A_1 \qquad \text{(VI-15b)}$$

This is tl.e equation for the condition of secular equilibrium. The daughter activity does not pass through a maximum in this case but reaches a constant value after which the rates of decay and formation are equal. Secular equilibrium means equality of disintegration rate between parent and daughter but not equality in the number of atoms of each present. The relationship between the number of atoms of each is seen very clearly in Equation (VI-15a) to be dependent on the relative half lives.

The length of time of observation of the activity of a sample may be the determining factor as to whether it will appear to be transient or secular equilibrium. For a parent with a 1 month half life, observation over a few days will seem to be secular equilibrium, whereas observation over a 3 month period will show transient equilibrium. If there are more than 2 active members in the chain, it is possible to calculate the amount of any intermediate present at any time but the equations are more complicated than need be considered here.

Units of Activity

The curie has been defined as the standard unit of activity. It was first defined as equal to the disintegration rate of the quantity of radon in equilibrium with 1 gram of radium. However, since this value changed slightly from time to time as better measurements of this quantity were made, the decision was made to fix the value of the curie at 3.7×10^{10} dps.

Experimental

Experiment 10 should be begun early in the course, possibly after Experiment 4, as it will be necessary to count the samples over sufficient periods of time to observe decay over several half life periods. During this time variations in count rate may occur due to a number of causes such as geometry, tube aging, and voltage fluctuations. A sample of Cs^{137} will show no decay over this period of several months so if it is counted each time along with the samples, by assuming a constant activity for the cesium sample, it is possible to obtain a correction factor for each counting period. This procedure will not correct for all causes of variation but is recommended as a check on the operational behavior of the counting system for determinations made at intervals over long periods of time.

The concept of secular equilibrium is demonstrated in Experiments 11 and 12. In both cases, the relationship between Sr^{90} and Y^{90} is studied but the separation techniques are different. Further examples of radioactive equilibrium will be encountered in later experiments (Nos. 17, 21, 26, 28, and 30) where the half lives will be rather short. In Experiment 11, ion exchange resin is used to effect the separation of the Sr-Y activities. For the theory behind the operation of ion exchange resins in separations,

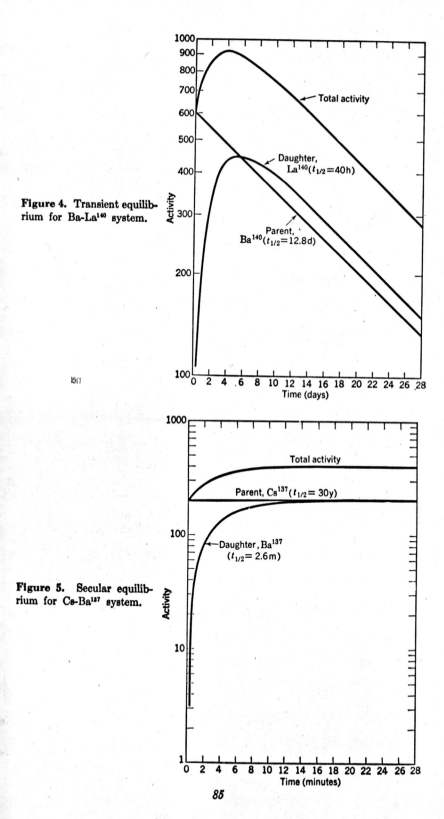

Figure 4. Transient equilibrium for Ba-La^{140} system.

Figure 5. Secular equilibrium for Cs-Ba^{137} system.

Chapter IX should be consulted. Actually, in this experiment the resin is not used in the normal fashion whereby separation is achieved by a difference in the affinity of anionic species for the cationic (in this case, quaternary ammonium) resin groups. In this instance the preliminary washing with NaOH serves to replace all other anionic groups with hydroxyl ions. The result will be a very high concentration of hydroxyl ions in and around each resin bead. As the Sr-Y solution moves through the resin bed, upon reaching the region of high pH, the yttrium precipitates as $Y(OH)_3$ but the strontium keeps on moving down the bed as its hydroxide is more soluble. Upon elution of the strontium, the yttrium is removed by elution with a 1.0 N solution of hydrochloric acid which lowers the pH and dissolves the $Y(OH)_3$ precipitate. One advantage of this technique is that it makes it possible to utilize the difference in solubilities of the hydroxides of strontium and yttrium to separate the pair without having to add an inert carrier such as the iron in Experiment 12. The use of anion exchange resins in the sulfide form has been shown to cause similar precipitation of tracer amounts of elements with insoluble sulfides. Since the cation concentration is so low in these tracer levels, this implies a very high anion concentration around (or within) the resin beads.

The theory of coprecipitation (Experiment 12) is discussed in Chapter IX. Coprecipitation is one of the oldest and most widely used of radiochemical separation procedures.

For the first time in this course, these experiments require the student to transfer volumes of solution in the milliliter range. Simple transfer pipets such as the one depicted in Figure 6 may be made very easily with

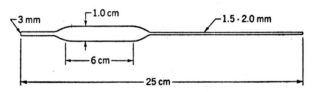

Figure 6. Transfer pipet.

only a minimal amount of training in glass handling techniques. The heated portion of a section of glass tubing of 1 cm I.D. is drawn out for several inches to form a sturdy, slim neck. The tubing is broken at this neck and a long, thin section pulled out about 7 cm down the tubing opposite the neck. This thin section is cut so as to leave it about 15 cm long. The short neck is inserted in the hypodermic syringe in the same fashion as the micropipets. A number of these transfer pipets should be made and kept on hand. The advantage of such a simple device is that it may (and should) be discarded after a single use so that there is no possibility of cross contamination of experiments from use of an improperly cleaned pipet.

EXPERIMENT 10

Half Life Determination

Method:

Prepare samples of I^{131}, S^{35} and P^{32} on counting discs by pipetting a sufficient quantity of stock solution to give approximately 5000 cpm on either of the top two shelves of the Geiger-Müller sample holders. Fix the activity permanently, after drying under a heat lamp, by spraying lightly with Krylon spray over the top of the disc. A solution of cellulose acetate in acetone may be substituted for the Krylon. Count the samples with the Geiger-Müller counter sufficiently long to collect 10,000 total counts. Take a background also. (Samples of I^{131} and P^{32} may be used from Experiment 8.)

Prepare a Cs^{137} sample and count it each time also. Use this as a check against fluctuation in count rate due to tube aging, voltage changes, etc. Obtain a correction factor after subtraction of background, from the Cs^{137} count for each counting period and apply to the I, S, and P count rates.

Continue to count these samples each period until the end of the semester in the same fashion. Plot a curve of log cpm versus time, taking the initial count as zero time. Ascertain the best $t_{1/2}$ for each activity from your curves after resolution of the curve for any other longer lived activities.

EXPERIMENT 11

Radioactive Equilibrium

Purpose:

To study the growth and decay curves for Y^{90} daughter from the Sr^{90} parent.

Method:

Prepare an anion resin column for the separation by loading an aqueous slurry of Dowex-1 anion resin into a glass column of 3 mm I.D. until the resin bed is 5 cm in length (Figure 4, Ch. IX). Be sure that a small wad of glass wool is first placed in the tip of the glass column before adding any resin. Run 3 ml of $2 N$ NaOH solution through the resin bed, then 1 ml of H_2O. Add an aliquot of tracer Sr^{90}-Y^{90} solution containing between 5000–10,000 cpm to a glass counting disc containing 2 drops of 0.1 N HCl. Then with a transfer pipet, transfer the total volume to the top of the resin bed as quantitatively as possible. (Caution: Pull the liquid only part way up the pipet stem; avoid touching the column walls with the pipet tip as much as possible.) Begin catching the drops off the bottom of the column tip—4 drops to a counting plate. After the liquid level has fallen even with the top of the resin bed, add two more drops of 0.1 N HCl to the glass disc and then transfer as before to the resin bed. Then, when the liquid is all in the resin, add 2 more drops of 0.1 N HCl directly on the resin bed. Follow this with 20 more drops of 0.1 N HCl. Dry each counting plate after 4 drops are collected and count in a Geiger-Müller counter. When the activity level falls to background again on the counting discs, remove the 0.1 N HCl remaining above the resin column and add 1 N HCl. For both solutions, the flow rate should be approximately 2 minutes per drop. Continue catching 4 drops per plate until the second activity is eluted from the resin. Prepare a sample of the same aliquot of the Sr-Y stock solution as used in the elution.

Data:

Plot the cpm versus the plate number. The first peak is the Sr^{90}, the second is the Y^{90}.

Take the most active plate from each peak and count them and the initial aliquot with and without an aluminum absorber of approximately 200 mg/per cm^2 in the Geiger-Müller counter. Take the background with and without this absorber. Continue to count these three samples with and without the absorber every 2 to 3 days over a 3 week period. Then, analyze the activity versus time plots and discuss the observations and their interpretations. Treat the data from the first peak as a case of secular equilibrium and analyze the graph for:

(a) the total activity (Sr + Y),
(b) the Sr^{90} activity alone,
(c) the growth of the Y^{90} activity.

From the data of the second peak, determine the half life of Y^{90}.

EXPERIMENT 12

Radioactive Equilibrium

Purpose:

To use coprecipitation to separate a daughter activity from its parents. Y^{90} is separated from Sr^{90}.

Method:

(1) Prepare a solution of 0.1 N HCl, 1 mg per ml of Sr^{++} carrier, and 1 mg per ml of Fe^{+++} carrier. Add approximately 20,000 cpm of the Sr^{90}-Y^{90} tracer to 1 ml of this solution. Warm the solution in a centrifuge cone in a hot water bath, and add, by drops, concentrated ammonium hydroxide until the precipitate fails to redissolve upon stirring, then add one more drop. Continue warming the solution until the coagulation of Fe(OH)$_3$ is satisfactory. Then, centrifuge the solution for 1 minute. Remove the supernatant solution with a transfer pipet, and wash the precipitate by stirring it in 0.5 ml of H$_2$O. Add this wash supernatant liquid to the first after centrifugation. Dissolve the Fe(OH)$_3$ precipitate by addition of 0.5 ml of 1 N HCl, then reprecipitate the Fe(OH)$_3$ with concentrated NH$_4$OH added by drops as before. After coagulation, centrifuge and remove the supernatant liquid, then wash the precipitate with 1.0 ml portions of water and centrifuge. Redissolve the Fe(OH)$_3$ precipitate in a minimum amount of HCl and transfer the solution to a counting planchet. Record the time of separation.

(2) Warm the supernatant solution from the first precipitation and add 0.2 ml of a 1 M (NH$_4$)$_2$SO$_4$ solution while stirring. Warm the solution in the water bath to coagulate the SrSO$_4$, then pour the solution through the filter assembly and wash with two portions each of 0.1 ml aliquots of water, alcohol and acetone. Mount this sample in the same fashion as the Fe(OH)$_3$ sample.

(3) Prepare a sample of the same aliquot of the Sr-Y stock solution as used in the separation.

Count the samples from 1, 2, and 3 each with and without an aluminum absorber of approximately 200 mg/cm^2 in a Geiger-Müller counter. Take the background both with and without this absorber. Sample 1 should be Y^{90}, Sample 2, Sr^{90} and Sample 3, an equilibrium mixture of Sr and Y. The absorber should allow only Y^{90} to count, whereas the non-absorber count is both Y^{90} and Sr^{90}. From these initial counts, calculate the yields of the precipitation steps.

Continue to count these samples every 2 to 3 days over a 3 week period both with and without the absorber. Then plot log [cpm—background] versus time without and with absorber for Samples 1 and 2. Analyze the curves as directed in the previous experiment.

PROBLEMS

1. What is the weight of the active species in samples containing 1 millicurie of activity for I^{131}, P^{32}, Co^{60}, freshly separated U^{238}?

2. Calculate the number of atoms and the weight of the Pm^{147} sample whose absolute disintegration rate was determined in Experiment 7 (Chapter V).

3. What is the count rate of a sample 9 half lives after a rate of 10^7 cpm is measured?

4. In a sample of $_{98}Cf^{252}$, the measured total half life is 2.6 years. If the ratio of spontaneous fission events to alpha decays is 3 to 97, what is the partial half life of $_{98}Cf^{252}$ to spontaneous fission decay?

5. Calculate the energy released in 1 day by a 1 gram source of $_{94}Pu^{239}$ if $Q = 5.24$ Mev and the half life of Pu^{239} is 24,400 years.

6. If a freshly prepared sample of $_{82}Pb^{212}$ of 10^6 dpm is allowed to stand for 2 hours, what will be the total disintegration rate at the end of that time?

$$Pb^{212} \xrightarrow[10.6h]{\beta^-} Bi^{212} \xrightarrow[60.5\ m]{\beta^-} Po^{212} \xrightarrow[3 \times 10^{-7}s]{\alpha} Pb^{208}$$

7. Make a plot of the total disintegration rate as a function of time for a freshly separated sample of $_{58}Ce^{144}$ for the first 2 hours after separation.

8. The following data were taken with a Geiger-Müller counter:

t(hr)	dpm	t(hr)	dpm	t(hr)	dpm
0	7000	10	2300	30	590
1	6000	12.5	1850	35	450
2	5300	15	1500	40	340
3	4600	17.5	1250	45	260
5	3800	20	1060	50	200
7.5	2860	25	780		

Resolve these data into two activities and ascertain their half lives.

9. If a kilogram of U^{238} is purified and then set aside for 2 months, what weight of Th^{234} will be present in the uranium sample at the end of that time?

$$_{92}U^{238} \xrightarrow[4.5 \times 10^9 y]{\alpha} {}_{90}Th^{234} \xrightarrow[24.1d]{\beta^-} {}_{91}Pa^{234}$$

10. Calculate the radiation dose (in rems) received in a day by 2 grams of thyroid tissue containing 1 mc of I^{131}. Assume that the average beta energy of I^{131} is 280 kev.

REFERENCES

Evans, R. D., *The Atomic Nucleus.* New York: McGraw-Hill Book Co., Inc., 1955, Chapter 15.

Friedlander, G., and J. W. Kennedy, *Nuclear and Radiochemistry.* New York: John Wiley & Sons, Inc., Chapter 5.

Glasstone, S., *Sourcebook on Atomic Energy.* New York: D. Van Nostrand Co., 1950, Chapter 5.

Halliday, D., *Introductory Nuclear Physics.* New York: John Wiley & Sons, Inc., 1955, Chapter 4.

Lapp, R. E., and H. L. Andrews, *Nuclear Radiation Physics.* Englewood Cliffs, N. J.: Prentice-Hall, Inc., 1954, Chapter 5.

VII

Scintillation Spectrometry

MEASUREMENT of ionizing radiations by gas-filled detectors was discussed in an earlier chapter. In 1908, before the use of gas filled detectors had been developed, Rutherford and Geiger established the reliability of a method of counting alpha particles by observing by eye the flashes of luminescence produced in a thin layer of ZnS by the alpha particles. However, since the visual observation necessary with this system was tedious, counting by use of proportional or Geiger detectors was the only practical method until the development of a reliable electronic means of detecting and amplifying these small light scintillations. About 1946, photomultiplier tubes became available which could do this successfully, and the development of scintillation counting techniques has played an important role in nuclear science since that time.

Theory of Scintillators

Following the excitation of a molecule or an ion to an excited state through the absorption of energy, the decay back to lower levels and finally to the ground state may result in the emission of radiant energy with a wave length in the visible or near visible region of the spectrum. When this occurs, the substance possesses the property of luminescence. If this emission occurs within 10^{-8} sec after the initial excitation (this is the lifetime for an excited atomic state), it is termed fluorescence; if the lifetime of the emission is greater than 10^{-8} sec, in some cases even minutes, it is known as phosphorescence. Examples of luminescence are found in both inorganic and organic substances and in all the physical states of matter.

In organic crystals, the absorption of energy raises the molecule to one of the vibrational levels of an excited electronic state. By the dissipation of energy as heat through lattice vibrations, the molecule decays to a lower vibrational level of the excited electronic state. After 10^{-8} sec, a time sufficient for many molecular vibrations, the molecule may return to the ground electronic state with emission of a light photon. Since the energy necessary to promote the molecule to an excited state is, in general, larger than that emitted in any single step upon decay back to the ground state, reabsorption of these emitted photons is unlikely. Consequently, the crystal will be transparent to the emitted luminescent photons. Fluorescence is found usually in aromatic hydrocarbons such as anthracene and stilbene which have resonance structures.

Liquid and solid solutions of organic substances such as p-terphenyl will luminesce also. In these systems, the energy absorbed through the interaction of radiation with the solvent molecules is transferred rapidly by the latter to the solute which undergoes excitation and fluorescence as described in the preceding paragraph. The exact mechanism of the transfer of energy from solvent to solution is not known.

It is necessary to have small amounts of impurities in inorganic crystals to have luminescence. In ionic crystals in the ground state, all the electrons will lie in a lower valence band of energies. Excitation will promote electrons into a higher conduction band of energies. A band of forbidden levels separates the valence and conduction bands. Normally, electrons cannot exist in this forbidden band, but if there are impurities in the crystal lattice, at the sites of these imperfections allowed electron levels may be formed in the forbidden band. Following excitation to the conduction band through absorption of energy, the electron may move through this band until it reaches an impurity site. At this point it can decay to one of the electron levels in the forbidden band. De-excitation from this level back to the valence band may occur through phosphorescent photon emission. Since this photon will have an energy smaller than the difference between the valence and conduction bands, these crystals will be transparent to their own radiations. This transparency is a necessary property if the emitted scintillations are to be detected by an external photomultiplier tube.

Advantages of Scintillation Counting

The system used in scintillation counting is shown schematically in Figure 1. For successful operation, the following events must take place.

The nuclear radiation must be absorbed in the scintillator with subsequent re-emission of light photons. These photons must be transmitted in reasonable yield to the photocathode of the photomultiplier. Here the absorption of the light photons must result in the emission of electrons. The successive stages of the photomultiplier tube must multiply the number of electrons sufficiently to deliver a pulse at the output large enough to be handled adequately by the remainder of the electronic system.

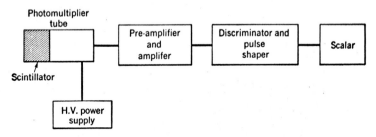

Figure 1. Schematic diagram of a scintillation counting system.

A Geiger counting system is less expensive than a scintillation system as the high voltage power supply need not be as well regulated in the former and no amplification of the tube output is needed. Since for alpha and beta particles in proportional counters and for the latter in Geiger counters, the efficiency is essentially 100%, there is little need for a scintillation system for ordinary count rate measurements of these emissions. However, gamma ray detection efficiency will be nearly a hundredfold greater for a solid crystal detector than for the gas-filled systems. Other advantages of a scintillation system are the capacity to handle higher counting rates because of very short resolving times (a few microseconds) and the ability to differentiate between different types of radiation. Normally, in scintillation systems it is not the phosphor or photomultiplier tube that determines the resolving time, but rather it is the electronic system. Of great importance is the fact that the light output is proportional to the energy absorbed in the phosphor. These advantages have led to widespread utilization of scintillation techniques in gross gamma counting, and in counting of all types of emissions in experiments conducted with accelerators or reactors where very high counting rates are encountered or where it is necessary to discriminate between various types of radiations. But perhaps the most widespread use of scintillation counters is for the measurement of the energy spectrum of gamma ray emitting samples.

Scintillators

To be useful as a scintillator, a substance must possess certain properties. First, there must be a reasonable probability for the absorption of energy.

Since the usual system uses solid or liquid scintillators, this condition is met easily. Following absorption the emission of luminescent radiation must occur with a high efficiency. As explained earlier, the scintillator must be transparent to its own radiations. Finally, these radiations must have a wave length which falls within the spectral region to which the photomultiplier tube is sensitive.

There are four types of phosphors which are used most frequently, inorganic crystals, organic crystals, liquid solutions such as *p*-terphenyl in xylene and solid solutions such as terphenyl in polystyrene. Some characteristic properties of the most common are listed in Table I.

TABLE I

Properties of Some Common Phosphors

Material	Density (g/cm^3)	Wave length of maximum emission (Å)	Decay time for emission (seconds)	Relative pulse height (from β particles)
Inorganic				
NaI(Tl)*	3.67	4100	2.5×10^{-7}	210
ZnS(Ag)*	4.10	4500	1×10^{-5}	200
Organic				
Anthracene	1.25	4400	3.2×10^{-8}	100
Stilbene	1.16	4100	6×10^{-9}	60
Plastic phosphors	1.06	3500–4500	$3–5 \times 10^{-9}$	28–48
Liquid phosphors	0.86	3550–4500	$2–8 \times 10^{-9}$	27–49

* (Tl) and (Ag) indicate small amounts of these elements added as impurity activators.

These data indicate that the greater density of the inorganic crystals make them superior for gamma-ray counting. The resolving time is shorter for the organic systems, whether liquid or solid. When large detector volumes are necessary, a liquid solution system is the simplest and most economical to use.

ZnS(Ag) is the common phosphor for alpha detection. For electrons, anthracene is used whereas for gamma rays, sodium iodide is the choice. The impurity activator in NaI crystals is thallium. The crystal shows a uniform response in light emission per unit energy absorbed over a range of thallium concentration from 0.1 to 1%. LiI(Eu), lithium iodide, europium activated, has been used to count low energy neutrons. For heavy charged particles, electrons and mesons, crystals of CsI(Tl) may be used. KI(Tl) is not hygroscopic as is NaI(Tl); however, the natural background in such a crystal due to the small amount of K^{40} present is a serious disadvantage. ZnS(Ag) does not possess a high transparency to its own radiation and can be used only in thin layers.

It is necessary to shield the scintillator–photomultiplier system from external light. It is also necessary to provide good optical coupling between the phosphor and the photomultiplier so that the emitted photons will be

transmitted to the photocathode in high yield. Anthracene crystals may be cemented directly on the photomultiplier window with Canada balsam and the whole assembly wrapped with thin aluminum foil to keep out ambient light. Since sodium iodide is hygroscopic, it is hermetically sealed in an aluminum jacket on all but one face where a glass window replaces the aluminum. This window is coupled to the tube window with Dow Corning DC-200, a high viscosity silicone oil.

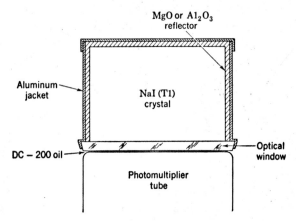

Figure 2. A sodium iodide crystal canned and mounted on a photomultiplier.

The emission of luminescence will be isotropic wherever it occurs in the phosphor. The photons traveling to the walls must have a high probability of reflection if the transmission to the phototube is to occur in high yield. At the phosphor-tube interface, some of the photons will be transmitted and the remainder reflected. The latter must be minimized by choosing a phosphor with the proper refractive index. Calcium tungstate is a good crystal phosphor except for a high internal reflection. The phosphors in Table I have acceptable indices of refraction. For NaI(Tl) crystals, a thin layer of powdered MgO or α-alumina is placed between the crystal surface and the aluminum can to increase reflection both of the photons emitted towards the walls and those reflected back from the window.

In some cases a length of lucite-polymethyl-methacrylate is interposed between the tube and phosphor. This serves as a light pipe to transmit the emitted photons over short distances. The considerations of the previous paragraphs concerning proper optical coupling at interfaces must be applied to the light pipe interfaces, also.

The Photomultiplier

In anthracene crystals approximately 10 photons are emitted for each 1000 ev of beta energy absorbed by the crystal. As Table I shows, the photon yield is twice as large in NaI and one half as large in stilbene for the same energy loss. Of the photons which reach the sensitive photocathode of the tube, on the average one photoelectron will be ejected for each 10 photons. This photocathode, located on the inside of the tube window, is most commonly an intermetallic compound of cesium and antimony, Cs_3Sb. The photoelectrons are accelerated to the first dynode stage of the phototube. As these electrons strike the dynode surface, they cause the emission of secondary electrons in large numbers. These secondary elec-

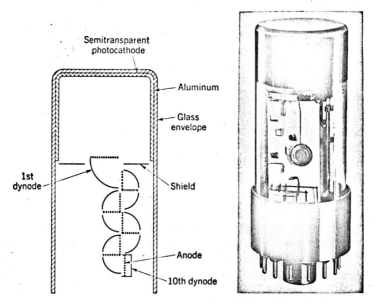

Figure 3. Photomultiplier tube Du Mont 6292: schematic diagram and photograph. [G. A. Morton, *Proceedings of the International Conference on the Peaceful Uses of Atomic Energy*, **14**, 246, United Nations, New York (1956); photo courtesy Allen B. Du Mont Laboratories, Inc.]

trons are accelerated to the second dynode stage where once again electron multiplication occurs. In this fashion the current is multiplied consecutively at each of the dynodes. The total current multiplication will be given by n^a where a is the total number of dynode stages and n is the multiplication factor at each stage. Since a is normally 10 and the average value of n between 4 and 5, the total multiplication is $2 - 8 \times 10^6$. The voltage difference between each dynode is 100–300 volts. The multiplication in the phototube is very sensitive to the dynode voltages; therefore, it is necessary to have stability in the high voltage power supply to at least 0.1%. Mu metal shields are used to shield the photomultiplier from external magnetic fields. The multiplied current is changed to a pulse of a few volts at the input of the preamplifier. The output from the latter may

be fed directly into the Geiger-Müller tube input on most scalars for simple counting.

The photocathodes of commercially available tubes have a spectral sensitivity range which includes the wave lengths of NaI (3500–5000Å) and anthracene (4300–4900Å) emissions. Figure 3 shows a photomultiplier tube in common use.

Well Counters

For the counting of gamma-emitting liquid samples, NaI(Tl) crystals with a hole large enough to hold small test tubes are used. The total gamma absorption coefficient decreases with energy (see M_T in Figure 8) and so also will the counting efficiency as it is proportional to the absorption coefficient. The efficiency will fall off as the liquid volume increases beyond a few milliliters since the liquid level will begin to approach the top of the well.

Beta Spectrometry

Precise measurements of beta spectra may be made with instruments employing magnetic fields. The electrons are bent in their passage through

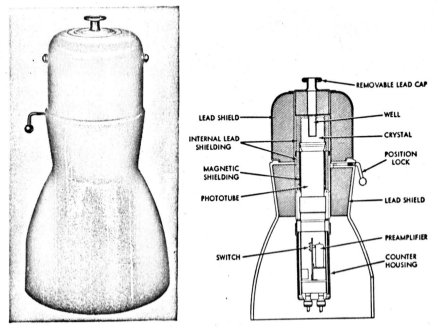

Figure 4. Well scintillation counter.
(*Courtesy Nuclear-Chicago Corp.*)

the region of the field according to the momentum with which they are
ejected from the nucleus. Either current collection devices (e.g., Geiger-
Müller counters) or photographic plates are used as the detection element.
Although capable of high precision and resolution, magnetic spectrometers
are expensive and require samples of rather high intensity as the electron
transmission is at best only a few per cent of the total. Scintillation crystal
spectrometry suffers from neither of these disadvantages although usually
neither the precision nor the resolution is as good as that of the magnetic
instruments.

For spectrometry it is necessary to add a linear amplifier to the system
in Figure 1 and to modify the discriminator so that there will be an upper
as well as a lower limit on the pulses accepted to be passed on to the scalar.
In single channel pulse-height analyzers, this window may be moved man-
ually or automatically through successive portions of the energy spectrum.
In multi-channel analyzers, a number of fixed windows simultaneously
count the pulses in different energy intervals and the output from each
interval is presented on a separate scaling unit. Analyzers of 20, 32, 100,
and 256 channels, as well as others, are available commercially.

Despite the fact that the relative photon emission (pulse height) is twice as
large for electrons in sodium iodide crystals as in anthracene, the latter are
utilized in beta spectrometry. The aluminum jacket which is necessary
on NaI(Tl) will absorb a relatively large number of low-energy electrons,
thus distorting the observed spectrum in that region. In addition, the high
density and large Z (for iodide) will cause greater backscatter from the
surface, particularly of the lower-energy electrons. Only 8% of an incident beam of electrons entering normal to the surface, is back scattered out
of anthracene whereas for NaI, the figure is 80–90%. In anthracene, the
scattering distortion can be minimized by collimating the beam of beta
particles and shaping the crystal, as shown in Figure 5. This shape serves
to promote capture of all but a very few of the backscattered electrons.

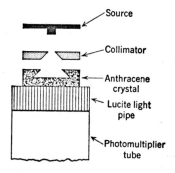

Figure 5. Arrangement for min-
imizing the loss of backscattered
electrons.

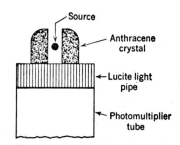

Figure 6. Split crystal arrangement for high-efficiency beta
spectrometry.

It is still necessary to correct for absorption by the air, reflector and any other material between the source and the crystal.

Another experimental arrangement places the sample between two separate crystals close together (Figure 6). This setup has a counting efficiency very close to 100% and should be capable of as accurate absolute beta counting as the 4π proportional counters. The data obtained with either experimental arrangement must be treated by making a Kurie Plot[1] if an accurate value of the maximum beta energy is to be obtained.

Gamma Spectrometry

Since gamma rays are not charged particles, they cannot undergo energy resolution by magnetic fields. Also, their range is too great to allow energy determinations requiring total capture of the gamma energy in gaseous detector systems. Consequently, pulse-height analysis of the light output from scintillation crystals is the technique used for gamma energy measurements. Unfortunately, there is more than one mode of energy dissipation for gamma rays, as we have seen in Chapter III. The result of this is a somewhat complicated energy spectrum even for a nuclide emitting a single gamma ray and it is necessary to reconsider these modes of interaction at this point in order to understand this spectrum.

(1) Photoelectric Effect: The result of this type of interaction is the production of photoelectrons with essentially the same energy as the gamma ray. The great majority of these electrons are completely stopped within the crystal so that the net process is complete deposition of the gamma energy in the crystal giving rise to a photopeak in the spectrum which is proportional to the E_γ.

(2) Compton Effect: In this case, only part of the energy of the gamma ray is transferred to the electron. The Compton electrons are stopped in the crystal and the scattered gamma ray may be absorbed by a photoelectric interaction or may escape the crystal. If the former occurs, the total energy deposited is again the E_γ and the pulse falls under the photopeak. However, if the gamma escapes without further interaction, only the energy of the Compton electron is deposited. This energy varies from essentially zero to a certain maximum value given by

$$E_e = \frac{4E_\gamma^2}{4E_\gamma + 1} \qquad\qquad \text{(VII-1)}$$

where E_γ is the energy of the incident gamma ray. As a result, a very broad Compton peak is present in a gamma spectrum, lower in energy than the photopeak.

[1] R. D. Evans, *The Atomic Nucleus* (McGraw-Hill Book Co., Inc., 1955), Chapter 17.

(3) Pair Production: When the gamma energy is greater than 1.02 Mev, a certain probability exists for the creation of a negatron (negative electron) and a positron. The negatron is stopped in the crystal; the positron loses energy until it is annihilated by conversion into two photons of 0.51 Mev each. This annihilation radiation, which is present in the spectrum of any positron emitter, may escape the crystal, or one or both photons may be captured. Consequently, pair production results in peaks in the spectrum corresponding to (1) the energy of the negatron, (2) this energy plus 0.51 Mev resulting from the capture of one photon, and (3) the negatron energy plus 1.02 Mev (i.e., the total E_γ) resulting from the capture of both photons of the annihilation radiation.

It is desirable to increase the photoelectric effect and to decrease the Compton effect so as to increase the number of events contributing to the photopeak. If lower-energy gammas are present, their photopeaks may be obscured by the Compton distribution from higher-energy gammas if these

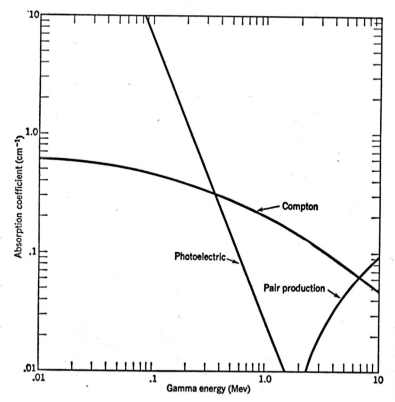

Figure 7. Dependence of absorption coefficients for sodium iodide on energy.

are very intense. With anthracene crystals, little resolution is seen in gamma spectra as the main contribution is from the Compton effect. Since the photoelectric effect absorption coefficient increases as the fifth power of Z, the use of NaI(Tl) crystals favors a much larger photopeak and over-all better resolution. Increasing the size of the crystal increases the probability of secondary photon capture and, therefore, the number of Compton events in which the scattered gamma also deposits its energy in the crystal. The increase in crystal dimensions results in an increase of the photopeak intensity at the expense of the Compton distribution.

For an ideal detector, a gamma spectrum would have the shape shown in Figure 8a, whereas the measured spectrum corresponds to that in Figure 8b. The broadening of the photopeak is due to many reasons, such as

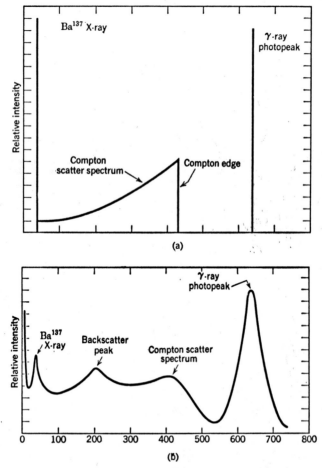

Figure 8. (a) Gamma spectrum from an ideal detector.
(b) Gamma spectrum from a real detector.

inhomogeneities in the crystal and variation in light reflection. However, the main cause of the broadening is found in the phototube where non-uniformity in the photocathode, fluctuations in the high voltage imposed on each dynode and the statistical variations in the small number of photo-electrons formed at the photocathode are all contributing factors. The broadening is measured by the value of the full width of the photopeak at one half of the maximum intensity divided by the pulse-height (or energy) value where the maximum occurs expressed in percentage. This value, termed the resolution, for the photopeak in Figure 8b is

$$\text{Resolution} = \frac{96}{800} \times 100 = 12\%$$

The resolution will be the governing factor in the ability of the system to differentiate between photopeaks of gamma rays of similar energies. Be-

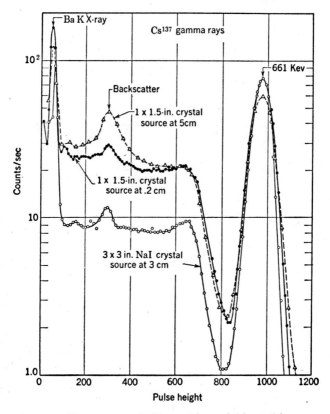

Figure 9. The response of 1½ in. × 1 in. and 3 in. × 3 in. crystals to gamma rays of Cs[137] and the response of the 1½ in. × 1 in. crystal with the source at some distance. [R. P. Bell, *Beta- and Gamma-Ray Spectroscopy*, chapter V, p. 141, Interscience (1955)]

cause the denominator is proportional to the energy, the resolution will decrease as the gamma energy increases.

The other features of the spectrum in Figure 8b are the backscatter peak, the X-ray peak and the noise peak. The backscatter peak arises from absorption in the crystal of scattered photons resulting from Compton interactions in the material surrounding the crystal and phototube. Obviously, the magnitude of this peak will be dependent on the distance of this material from the crystal (see Figure 9) and on the nature and amount of the material. The X-ray peak is due to the absorption of the X-rays emitted in the electronic rearrangement following the nuclear disintegration or following internal conversion. Bursts of very low energy electrons are emitted spontaneously from the photocathode and are the cause of the noise peak at very low discriminator settings. This limits the photon energies that can be studied to a minimum of several kev.

Experimental

In Chapter III, Experiments 2 and 3, the counting plateau was determined for Geiger and proportional counters. The counter voltage in these systems is the one applied to the two electrodes. For scintillation counters,

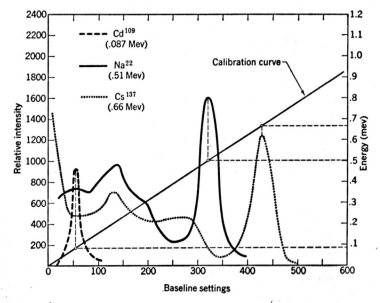

Figure 10. An illustration of the method of using gamma spectra curves to obtain a calibration curve for the base-line settings as a function of energy. The calibration curve is drawn through the points determined by the base-line settings and the energy of the photopeaks of the standards.

the counter voltage is the one applied to the photomultiplier tube. It is possible to obtain a counting plateau for a scintillation system which will be a function of the crystal size, the source and background scattering as well as the performance of the phototube.[2]

Rather than manual operation, a scintillation spectrometer may be operated by a constant speed scan through the spectrum using a motor driven potentiometer. In this case the discriminator output is fed to a count rate meter. The spectrum obtained from the rate meter is traced on a recorder. No matter how the spectrometer is operated, it is necessary to calibrate the spectrum with photopeaks of known energy. Standards may be purchased commercially but for the purposes of this course, it is entirely satisfactory to prepare the standards personally. For gamma standards, Na^{22} and Cs^{137} provide well defined photopeaks. Figure 10 demonstrates the calibration curve obtained using these two nuclides.

In Experiments 14 and 15 the sources may be placed directly on the crystal housing if this is necessary to obtain sufficient intensity. The instructor will supply the information on the proper high voltage and amplifier gain settings to be used. If at constant window width the gain is increased by a factor of two, the spectrum will be stretched over twice the voltage range. Unless this is necessary to better resolve two intense peaks of similar energy, the stretching out of the spectrum may reduce the maxima of low intensity peaks to the point where it is difficult to resolve them from the background.

EXPERIMENT 13

Scintillation Counting

Purpose:

To study the use of scintillation counters for routine counting.

Method:

(1) Run a plateau determination for the scintillation counter in the same fashion as Experiment 2, using a sample of either Cs^{137} or Na^{22}. If both anthracene and NaI(Tl) crystals are available, determine the plateau for each.

(2) If the counter is the well crystal type, use 0.5 ml of a 0.1 *N* HCl solution containing 5000–10,000 cpm of either Na^{22} or Cs^{137} for the plateau determination. Then, increase the solution volume 0.5 ml at a time and measure the count rate for each total volume (adding no additional activity) up to 5.0 ml. Count each volume to at least 1% probable error.

[2] R. W. Engstrom and J. L. Weaver, *Nucleonics*, **17**, 70 (February, 1959).

Measure the distance from the top of the well to the liquid level for each volume.

Data:

(1) Make a count rate versus voltage graph to determine the operating voltage from the plateau. Calculate the slope of the plateau in percentage and compare this with the slopes of the Geiger and proportional counter plateaus of Experiments 2 and 3.

(2) Plot the count rate as a function of the total volume. Briefly comment on the significance of this curve.

EXPERIMENT 14

Beta Spectrum Analysis

Purpose:

To determine the maximum beta energy using an anthracene crystal single channel pulse-height spectrometer.

Method:

Prepare a sample of Cs^{137} and one of Pm^{147} as in Experiment 8. Check with the instructor concerning the proper level of activity (approximately 50,000 cpm), the setting to be used for the amplifier gain controls and the method of mounting the sample with respect to the crystal.

With the window width set at 1 volt, turn the count switch on and slowly turn the base line dial starting just above the thermal noise level. Watch the scalar lights and note any peaks and the base line setting where the count rate falls to background. Then reset the base line back to the initial point and take a 0.5 minute count. Advance the base line 1 volt and take another 0.5 minute count. Repeat this procedure in 1 volt steps until the count rate drops below 50, being sure to cover all the features noted in the first scan.

Do this for both Pm^{147} and Cs^{137}, then remove both samples and run a background over the spectrum range in the same fashion. P^{32} is a good nuclide to run if it is available.

Caution:

Always disconnect the photomultiplier high voltage before removing the light shield from the detector assembly.

Data:

After subtraction of background, plot the count rate vs. the pulse height as read from the base line setting. Discuss the features of these curves.

The conversion electron peak in Cs^{137} may be used to calibrate the base line settings for energy.

Make an approximation to a Kurie plot by plotting (cpm/pulse height)$^{1/2}$ versus (pulse height) for both Cs^{137} and Pm^{147}. To correct the Cs^{137} curve in this plot for the contribution due to the conversion electron, extrapolate back from the non-linear, high energy end for the conversion electron contribution by assuming a Gaussian shape for the conversion electron peak. The values of the (cpm/pulse height)$^{1/2}$ are read off the extrapolated curve at several pulse heights and the cpm calculated. These values of cpm are subtracted from the total cpm at each pulse height and new (cpm/pulse height)$^{1/2}$ values calculated, using the corrected cpm values. A new "Kurie" plot is made and the best straight line drawn, ignoring, if necessary, the lowest energy points. From the base line-energy calibration, determine the maximum β energy for Pm^{147} and Cs^{137}.

EXPERIMENT 15

Gamma Spectrometry

Purpose:

To use a gamma-ray spectrometer to determine the gamma energies and decay scheme of radioactive nuclides.

Method:

Set the amplifier gain controls of the single channel analyzer as directed by the instructor. Position the source on the scintillation probe with the aid of the instructor. A NaI(Tl) crystal is used with an aluminum jacket sufficient to cut out electrons. Turn the count switch on after setting the window width at 1 volt, and slowly turn the base line dial. Watch the scalar lights and note the position of all peaks in the spectrum. Then, reset the base line to just above the noise level and, starting with that setting, take a 0.5 minute count in 1 volt steps throughout the spectrum seen in the scan.

Do this procedure for Na^{22} and Cs^{137}. If Cd^{109} is available, it may be run also. Then, determine the spectra for samples of Ce^{144} and Co^{60}. Finally, run a background for the spectral range covered in these measurements. Be sure that all sources other than the one being counted are removed sufficiently from the immediate vicinity of the crystal during the pulse-height analysis.

Caution:

If there is no automatic switch on the detector assembly, be certain to disconnect the photomultiplier high voltage before removing the light shield.

Data:

(1) Plot cpm after subtraction of background versus base line setting. Using the energies of Na^{22} as 0.505 and 1.28 Mev, of Cs^{137} as 0.662 Mev and of Cd^{109} as 0.087 Mev, calibrate the base line settings for energy (Figure 10).

(2) Identify all the peaks and humps in the Ce^{144} and Co^{60} spectra as to energy.

(3) Theoretically, the Compton peak associated with a photopeak has an energy given by Equation (VII-1). Locate the Compton peaks associated with the photopeaks in your spectra and compare the energies with the theoretically expected values.

(4) Calculate the source intensity N_0 for the Cs^{137} sample from the equation

$$N_0 = 4N'(R/r)^2$$

and $$N' = N(1 - e^{-\mu\rho t})^{-1}$$

where N = net total counts under (photopeak + Compton peak) minus the background,

t = crystal thickness,

ρ = density of NaI = 3.7 gm/cm²,

μ = total mass absorption coefficient in cm²/gm (Figure 7),

R = distance from source to center of crystal,

r = radius of NaI crystal,

N' = total number of gammas of energy E in solid angle $d\Omega$ subtended by the crystal with the source point as vertex.

(5) Calculate the energy resolution for the photopeak curves in all the spectra, assuming a Gaussian distribution shape for the photopeaks when necessary to resolve them from the Compton peaks.

$$\% \text{ Resolution} = \frac{\Delta E_{1/2}}{E} \times 100$$

Plot the resolution as a function of the energy of the photopeak.

REFERENCES

Bell, P. R., *Beta- and Gamma-ray Spectroscopy*. New York: Interscience Publishers, Inc., 1955, Chapter V.

Evans, R. D., *The Atomic Nucleus*. New York: McGraw-Hill Book Co., Inc., 1955, Chapters 23–25.

Handbook for Scintillation Spectrometry. Baird-Atomic, Inc., 1958.

Lapp, R. E., and H. L. Andrews, *Nuclear Radiation Physics*. Englewood Cliffs, N. J.: Prentice-Hall, Inc., 1954, Chapters 5 and 7.

Morton, G. A., *Proceedings of the International Conference on the Peaceful Uses of Atomic Energy* (Geneva: United Nations), 14, 246 (1956).

Price, W. J., *Nuclear Radiation Detection*. New York: McGraw-Hill Book Co., Inc., 1958.

Scintillation Phosphors. The Harshaw Chemical Co., 1958.

VIII

Neutron Activation

Preparation of Isotopes

Radioactive isotopes may be prepared by a wide variety of reactors and accelerators; however, only cyclotrons and nuclear reactors of at least moderate flux produce a sufficiently high specific activity (disintegrations per minute per gram of the element) to be of practical interest as isotope producers. Fortunately, these two methods of production supplement each other in that they do not, in general, produce the same isotopes. In cyclotrons, charged particles such as protons, deuterons, and alphas bombard the target nuclei and after emission of one or more particles to remove the excess energy, a radioactive nuclide may remain. Usually the emitted particles are neutrons. It is of great importance that the capture of a positively charged particle and subsequent emission of neutrons result in isotopes which are neutron deficient compared to the stable isotopes of the particular element. The stable isotopes in the table of nuclides represent those which are stable with respect to both positive and negative beta decay. The lighter or neutron deficient isotopes such as those usually produced in cyclotron irradiation decay by either positron emission (β^+) in the low atomic number elements or orbital electron capture in the heavier elements. Both decay processes are present in the middle weight elements. Another important point in cyclotron bombardments is that the product is not usually isotopic with the target, thus providing a method for the production of activities which are not diluted by the presence in macro amounts of non-radioactive isotopes of the element. Even when the same activity may be made in a reactor, the cyclotron production may be favored because of this carrier free aspect despite the greater cost. An example of an important cyclotron produced radioisotope is sodium-22 by the reaction

$$_{12}Mg^{24} + {_1}d^2 = {_{11}}Na^{22} + {_2}He^4$$

This same reaction is written in nuclear reaction shorthand

$$Mg^{24}(d, \alpha)Na^{22}$$

Other important cyclotron reactions are

$$Cr^{52}(d, 2n)Mn^{52}$$

$$Fe^{56}(d, \alpha)Mn^{54}$$

$$Fe^{57}(d, n)Co^{58}$$

Nuclear reactors maintain themselves by chain fission reactions propagated by neutrons. If foreign materials are introduced into the reactor, neutrons may be absorbed producing neutron rich isotopes, frequently radioactive in nature. In the great majority of cases, these neutron capture reactions produce activities isotopic with the target material, and, since they are heavier than the stable isotopes, they decay by negatron (β^-) emission. A second mode of production in reactors is by fission itself, as the majority of fission products will be radioactive and will cover a wide range of atomic numbers in varying abundances. These activities may be isolated carrier free. However, in fission products 1 or 2 activities must be isolated from a relatively large number of other activities and may present a formidable separation and purification problem.

Radioactive isotopes may be produced indirectly as daughters of parent activities made in one of the ways already discussed. Thus strontium-90 with a 27.7 year half life will be produced in fission and in turn will produce by beta decay yttrium-90 (64.2 hour half life) throughout the lifetime of the former.

Which mode of production is utilized is the result of many factors. The distance from the production site in shipping time, the length in time of separation and purification processes and of the experiment itself determine the half life with which it is practical to work. This determines in turn which isotope must be used. For example, if these three time determining processes indicate the necessity for a half life of at least several weeks, for sodium this eliminates the possibility of using the reactor produced sodium-24 (15.0 hours) and necessitates use of the cyclotron pro-

duced sodium-22 (2.6 years). If the experiment requires the use of pure tracer, carrier-free activities, either cyclotron or fission product activities are called for. Because of the economics of the situation—in a cyclotron, only one target at a time may be irradiated—reactor activities are to be preferred whenever possible and are usually much easier to obtain on a routine basis.

Reaction Cross Sections

The probability of a reaction occurring between a target nucleus and a projectile to form a different product nuclide is expressed as the cross section of that reaction. The cross section σ is given the units of area. If the cross section for a particular reaction is known, it is possible to calculate the number of product nuclei by the equation

$$N_2 = I_0 (1 - e^{-n\sigma x}) \qquad \text{(VIII-1)}$$

where N_2 is the number of product nuclei, I_0 is the initial intensity of particles incident on the target, n is the number of target nuclei per cubic centimeter, and x is the target thickness in centimeters. If the target is sufficiently thin in relation to the beam, so that there is no significant decrease in intensity in traversing the target, the equation reduces to

$$N_2 = I_0 n\sigma x \qquad \text{(VIII-2)}$$

If I_0 is replaced by ft where f is the flux, i.e., the number of incident beam particles per second, and t is the time in seconds, and nx is replaced by N_1, the total number of target nuclei per square centimeter (compare with the units for absorber thicknesses), then

$$N_2 = N_1 \sigma ft \qquad \text{(VIII-3)}$$

The rate of growth may be expressed by

$$\frac{dN_2}{dt} = N_1 \sigma f \qquad \text{(VIII-4)}$$

If the product is radioactive, the situation is somewhat analogous to the considerations of parent-daughter relations in Chapter VI, and the rate of growth is given by

$$\frac{dN_2}{dt} = N_1 \sigma f - \lambda_2 N_2 \qquad \text{(VIII-5)}$$

which is seen to be similar to Equation (VI-10a). Solution of Equation (VIII-5) for the boundary condition of $N_2 = 0$ at $t = 0$, yields

$$N_2 = \frac{N_1 \sigma f}{\lambda_2} (1 - e^{-\lambda_2 t}) \qquad \text{(VIII-6a)}$$

$$A_2 = N_1 \sigma f (1 - e^{-\lambda_2 t}) \qquad \text{(VIII-6b)}$$

In some cases all the target nuclei will be within the area of the beam.

This is the case in a reactor where the total target and not only a portion of it is irradiated. In these cases, N_1 is defined as the total number of target nuclei present and f as the number of incident particles per square centimeter per second. Notice that this leaves the units of $N \cdot f$ unchanged. If the bombardment proceeds for a time $t \gg t_{1/2}$, a saturation activity level is reached and

$$A_2 = N_1 \sigma f \qquad \text{(VIII-7)}$$

This equation is valid when the value of N_1 is decreased only infinitesimally during the irradiation and f has the same value throughout the foil. At the other extreme, if $t \ll t_{1/2}$, then by expanding $e^{-\lambda t}$ in a Maclaurin's series,

$$A_2 = N_1 \sigma f (1 - [1 - \lambda_2 t])$$

$$A_2 = N_1 \sigma f \lambda_2 t \qquad \text{(VIII-8a)}$$

$$N_2 = N_1 \sigma f t \qquad \text{(VIII-8b)}$$

These equations lead to the realization that irradiation for a period of time equal to one half life produce an activity level equal to one half the saturation bombardment value and irradiation for 2 half lives produces $\frac{3}{4}$ the saturation value, and so on. The law of diminishing returns makes it impractical to continue the bombardment past 3 or 4 half life periods.

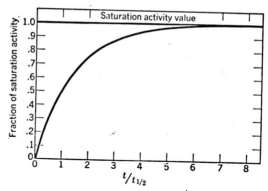

Figure 1. The rate of approach to saturation in production of a radioactive species as a function of the irradiation time in half life units.

A repulsive coulomb barrier exists for the entry of charged particles into nuclei; consequently, it is necessary that a beam of such particles have energies greater than this barrier for nuclear reactions to occur. This large amount of energy raises the nucleus to such a high energy level that one or more particles will be ejected in order to remove this excess energy from the nucleus. Gamma emission will also remove part of the excitation energy. For the heavier elements, the excitation energy may result in fission rather than simple particle emission.

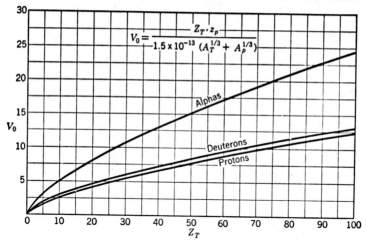

Figure 2. The coulomb barrier height as a function of Z_T, the atomic number of the target.

There is no coulomb barrier to entry of the neutrons into a nucleus; therefore, neutrons of essentially zero kinetic energy may cause nuclear reactions. In these cases, the excitation energy will be much lower—in fact, it will be equal to the binding energy released by the nucleus when the neutron is absorbed. This is the minimum energy necessary to re-emit a nucleon and it is quickly distributed among all the nucleons in the

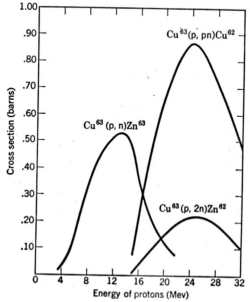

Figure 3. Cross sections for proton reactions with Cu^{63}.

nucleus. Since the probability of all this energy concentrating on a particular nucleon is quite low, de-excitation by gamma emission is the probable mode in these cases. Of course absorption of higher energy neutrons may result in nucleon emission just as for charged particles.

For many nuclei the cross section for neutron absorption varies inversely with the neutron velocity ($1/v$ law) for neutron energies up to several hundred electron volts. In the upper part and slightly beyond this energy region, neutron cross sections often have very high values for certain discrete neutron energies. This "resonance" capture occurs when the total excitation energy (binding energy + kinetic energy) exactly matches the energy of one of the excited nuclear levels. In indium a resonance absorption occurs for neutrons with a kinetic energy of 1.44 ev. The cross section at this energy is equal to $26{,}000 \times 10^{-24}$ cm^2 or 26,000 barns where the unit of a barn has the value 10^{-24} cm^2. This is the unit used for all types of nuclear cross sections. The maximum value for charged particle and higher energy neutron reactions is on the order of a few barns or less, whereas low energy neutrons may have cross sections very much higher.

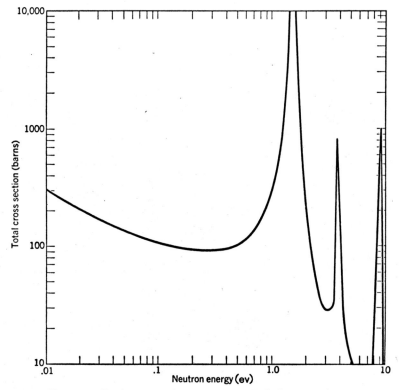

Figure 4. Total cross section for neutrons in indium as a function of their energy. (Adapted from Hughes and Harvey, *Neutron Cross Sections*)

Sources of Neutrons

The principal sources of neutrons are the nuclear reactors wherein fluxes of 10^9 to 10^{14} neutrons per second per square centimeter are common. In these reactors the neutrons are emitted in the fission process with energies as high as 14 Mev but the average is close to 1.5 Mev. Since it is desirable to increase the probability of capture by slowing the neutrons down, a moderator containing a low Z element with a low capture cross section surrounds the source. The neutrons suffer a large number of billiard ball-like collisions until equilibrium is established when, like the molecules of a gas, the neutrons will have a distribution of kinetic energies about the average value of $\frac{3}{2} kT$ (T is the temperature of the moderator). At room temperatures the energy of these thermal neutrons will be approximately 0.025 ev. The spectrum of energies of neutrons from a reactor will include both the fast neutron flux and the thermal or slow neutron flux. Table I

TABLE I

Thermal Neutron Cross Sections for Some Nuclides

Element	Z	A	Isotopic abundance (%)	Cross section (barns)	$t_{1/2}$ produced
Na	11	23	100	0.56	15.0 h
Al	13	27	100	0.21	2.27 m
P	15	31	100	0.23	14.3 d
K	19	41	6.9	1.0	12.4 h
Mn	25	55	100	13.4	2.6 h
Co	27	59	100	16	10.4 m(Co^{60m})
Br	35	79	50.5	2.9	4.4 h
				8.5	18 m
		81	49.5	3.5	35.9 h
Rh	45	103	100	12	4.5 m
				140	44 s
Ag	47	107	51.35	44	2.3 m
		109	48.65	110	24 s
In	49	115	95.8	145	54 m
I	53	127	100	5.5	25 m
Eu	63	151	47.8	1400	9.2 h
Dy	66	164	28.2	2600	1.3 m (Dy^{165m})
				1000	2.3 h (Dy^{165g})
Ho	67	165	100	60	27.3 h
Au	79	197	100	96	2.7 d

is a partial compilation of thermal neutron cross sections for a number of elements.

For smaller fluxes of neutrons, it is possible to use a source composed of radium (or polonium) intimately mixed with beryllium. The alpha particles from radium and its daughters have sufficient energy to react with beryllium to cause emission of a neutron.

(a) $$_{88}\text{Ra}^{226} \longrightarrow {}_{86}\text{Rn}^{222} + {}_2\text{He}^4$$

(b) $$_4\text{Be}^9 + {}_2\text{He}^4 \longrightarrow {}_6\text{C}^{12} + {}_0n^1$$

From a gram of radium plus daughters, approximately 10^{11} alphas per second produce on the order of 10^7 neutrons per second. It is necessary to surround the source with paraffin or water to thermalize the neutrons. It is also necessary to provide shielding to absorb the gamma radiation accompanying the neutron production. Commonly, these Ra-Be sources have 5 mg of radium so the total flux is on the order of 50,000 neutrons per second, with a total thermal flux of 200 neutrons per second.

Such a low flux limits production of measurable amounts of radioactivity to nuclides of at least moderate cross sections, short half lives and high isotopic abundance.

Activation Analysis

There has been increasing interest in the use of neutron capture reactions to measure trace impurities which have active capture products. With moderately high neutron fluxes of 10^{12} neutrons per cm^2 per second, the sensitivity for detection of many elements is sufficient to allow measurement of impurities present in a few parts per million and even a few parts per billion in some cases. The cross section, the isotopic abundance and the half life are determining factors as well as flux and counting efficiency. The use of gamma-ray scintillation spectrometry is a very valuable asset to activation analysis. In many cases, it is unnecessary to do any chemical separations, especially if gamma spectrometry is used, as interfering activities may be discriminated against. Usually a standard of known (and similar) composition is run with the unknown so that it becomes unnecessary to know the value of the flux and the detection efficiency. If the two samples are irradiated in the same position in the reactor for the same length of time and then are counted under identical conditions, the amount of impurity is given by

$$\frac{\text{Weight of impurity in unknown}}{\text{Weight of impurity in standard}} = \frac{\text{activity of impurity in unknown}}{\text{activity of impurity in standard}}$$

Second-order Capture

The cross section of the product nucleus may be sufficiently large that second-order capture products are formed during irradiations of moderate duration. If the first-order product is radioactive, then its concentration at any time is dependent on the decay constant and the cross section for

production of the second-order product as well as the cross section for its own production. A destruction constant may be defined as

$$\Lambda_2 = (\lambda_2 + f\sigma_2)$$

The number of atoms of the second-order product at time t is given by

$$N_3 = \Lambda_1 \Lambda_2^* N_1^0 \left[\frac{e - \Lambda_1 t}{(\Lambda_2 - \Lambda_1)(\Lambda_3 - \Lambda_1)} + \frac{e - \Lambda_2 t}{(\Lambda_1 - \Lambda_2)(\Lambda_3 - \Lambda_2)} \right.$$
$$\left. + \frac{e - \Lambda_3 t}{(\Lambda_1 - \Lambda_3)(\Lambda_2 - \Lambda_3)} \right] \quad \text{(VIII-9)}$$

where
$$\Lambda_1 = f\sigma_1$$
$$\Lambda_3 = \lambda_3$$
$$\Lambda_2^* = f\sigma_2$$

If a milligram of Tb_2O_3 is bombarded for 30 days at a flux of 10^{14} neutrons per cm^2 per second, the following processes occur

$$\sigma_1 = 45b \qquad \sigma_2 = 600b$$
$$Tb^{159}(n, \gamma) \, Tb^{160}(n, \gamma) \, Tb^{161}$$
$$\beta^- \downarrow \begin{array}{c} t_{1/2} \\ 72d \end{array} \qquad \beta^- \downarrow \begin{array}{c} t_{1/2} \\ 7.0d \end{array}$$

$$\Lambda_1 = 10^{14} \times 45 \times 10^{-24} = 4.5 \times 10^{-9}$$

$$\Lambda_2 = \left[\frac{0.693}{72 \times 24 \times 3600} + 10^{14} \times 600 \times 10^{-24} \right] = 1.7 \times 10^{-7}$$

$$\Lambda_2^* = 10^{14} \times 600 \times 10^{-24} = 6 \times 10^{-8}$$

$$\Lambda_3 = \frac{0.693}{7 \times 24 \times 3600} = 1.15 \times 10^{-6}$$

$$N_1^0 = \frac{6.02 \times 10^{23}}{366} \times 10^{-3} \times 2 = 3.28 \times 10^{18} \text{ atoms}$$

$$t = 30 \times 24 \times 3600 = 2.59 \times 10^6 \text{ sec}$$

Use of these values in equations (VIII-6) and (VIII-9) where Λ_2 replaces λ_2 in the former gives values of

      (1) 2.06×10^{11} dpm of Tb^{160}

      (2) 7.86×10^{10} dpm of Tb^{161}

Neutron Counters

Most neutron counters use detectors which contain BF_3 gas usually enriched in B^{10}. The neutron reacts with the boron such that

$$B^{10} + n \longrightarrow Li^7 + He^4 + Q$$

The recoiling Li^7 and He^4 dissipate their kinetic energy by ionization of the counting gas also present. The counter is operated in the proportional region so that the smaller pulses resulting from any gamma background may be discriminated against.

Szilard-Chalmers Reaction

The momentum imparted to a nucleus in a nuclear reaction with a charged particle or a fast neutron is almost invariably sufficient to result in the rupture of any chemical bonds holding the atom in a molecule. The same is true for the recoil energy imparted to a nucleus by the emission of an alpha particle. In the case of thermal neutron capture, the processes involved in the emission of the gamma ray necessary to remove the excitation energy impart recoil energy to the atom in excess of the 1 to 5 ev range of most chemical bond energies. Therefore, although the capture of the low energy neutron does not break the chemical bonds, the subsequent gamma emission does. In beta particle emission, the recoil energies are usually in the 1 to 5 ev range, also.

In (n, γ) processes, the target and product are isotopic. If, after rupture of the chemical bonds, the product atoms are capable of existence in a stable chemical state different and separable from that of the target atoms, the former may be isolated from the large mass of inactive target. This process is known as the Szilard-Chalmers reaction after the discoverers whose initial experiment is duplicated in Experiment 18.

A further requirement of a successful enrichment of specific activity by a Szilard-Chalmers process is that there not be rapid exchange between the active and the inactive atoms. If the reaction is

$$C_2H_5I + n \longrightarrow C_2H_5I^* + \gamma$$

the I* must be stabilized as an iodine atom or as an iodide ion. The thermal exchange reaction

$$C_2H_5I + I^* \rightleftharpoons C_2H_5I^* + I$$

must be very slow under the conditions of the experiment. During the process of recoiling, the I* loses energy by collisions resulting in excitation and ionization as described in Chapter III. This recoiling hot atom may in a collision replace an iodine or hydrogen atom from an ethyl iodide molecule so that exchange may also occur during the recoil process. The result is retention of the activity in the organic molecules. Retention is decreased by diluting the ethyl iodide with alcohol which allows the recoiling atom to be slowed down with fewer collisions with ethyl iodide molecules.

Three systems exhibiting Szilard-Chalmers reactions are studied in the experiments of this chapter. In addition to the (n, γ) process similar to that in ethyl iodide, in organic bromides a secondary Szilard-Chalmers

reaction follows isomeric transition decay. During neutron irradiation, the reaction is

$$RBr + n \underset{\sigma \approx 8.5\,b}{\overset{\sigma = 2.9\,b}{\rightleftharpoons}} \begin{cases} R + Br^{80m} \text{ (4.4hr)} \\ R + Br^{80g} \text{ (18m)} \end{cases}$$

Extraction by water of this bromide produces a sample of both Br^{80g} (Br^{80} in the lowest, or ground, state) and Br^{80m} (Br^{80} in an excited, or metastable, state). Both Br^{80m} and Br^{80g} also have some retention in the organic phase.

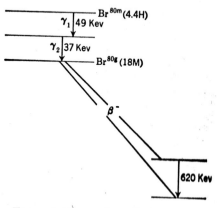

Figure 5. Decay scheme for bromine-80.

If, after a period of an hour, the extraction is repeated, only Br^{80g} is found in the aqueous sample. This Br^{80g} is a result of the reaction

$$RBr^{80m} \xrightarrow{\text{I.T.}} R + Br^{80g} + \gamma$$

The isomeric transitions which proceed by emission of a nuclear gamma ray do not provide sufficient recoil energy to break the C—Br bond. However, for this low energy transition the internal conversion process (Chapter III) is predominant. Internal conversion and Auger electron ejection results in a positive charge close to 5 for the bromine atom which provides sufficient excitation to dissociate the C—Br bond.

In addition to the organic halides, a number of inorganic systems demonstrate the Szilard-Chalmers reaction. From acid or neutral solutions of permanganate, most of the Mn^{56} activity is removable as MnO_2. From solid or dissolved chlorates, bromates, iodates, perchlorates and periodates, active halide samples may be isolated. Systems with Te, Se, As, Cu, and several of the Group VIII elements have been shown to be applicable to the Szilard-Chalmers process. The great advantage in all these cases is that a relatively small amount of activity may be isolated from a large mass of isotopic, inactive target. Because of retention, there will be some labeling of the target molecules, also.

Experimental

In the irradiations of indium, the cross section for indium has a value of 26,000 barns to neutrons of 1.44 ev energy. Therefore, in thick foil bombardments, it is necessary in precise calculations to take account of the decrease in flux at increasing depth in the foil due to neutron absorption. Cadmium has a very high cross section to thermal neutrons so that irradi-

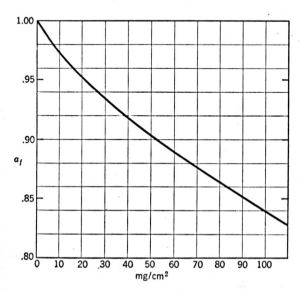

Figure 6. Correction factor a_f for indium as a function of foil thickness.

ation of indium wrapped with cadmium allows, in effect, activation of indium only by neutrons whose energy is above thermal values (epithermal), whereas irradiation of bare indium induces activation by the total neutron spectrum. The cadmium ratio (C.R.) for an indium foil of thickness x is defined as

$$\mathrm{C.R.}(x) = \frac{A(x)}{A_{\mathrm{Cd}}(x)}$$

$A(x) = $ Activity of bare foil $\left.\phantom{\rule{0pt}{2em}}\right\}$ for equal exposures
$A_{\mathrm{Cd}}(x) = $ Activity of Cd wrapped foil

The ratio of activities induced by the thermal flux to that by the epithermal flux in a zero thickness foil has been shown to be[1]

[1] Greenfield, Koontz, and Jarrett, *Nuclear Sci. and Eng.*, **2**, 246 (1057). Greenfield, Koontz, Jarrett, and Taylor, *Nucleonics*, **15**, 57 (March, 1957).

$$\left(\frac{A_{th}(0)}{A_{epi}(0)}\right) = 0.26 \left(\frac{A_{th}(x)}{A_{epi}(x)}\right)$$

$$= 0.26 \, [C.R.(x) - 1] \qquad \text{(VIII-10)}$$

This equation will be valid for indium foil thicknesses greater than 40 mg per cm^2. The activity from thermal neutron activation, $A_{th}(x)$, is calculated from the bare foil activation, $A_{th}(x) + A_{epi}(x)$, using

$$A_{th}(x) = A(x) \, \frac{[C.R. - 1]}{C.R.} \qquad \text{(VIII-11)}$$

To account for the flux depression in the foil, a_f from Figure 6 is used so that

$$A_{th}(0) = a_f A_{th}(x) \qquad \text{(VIII-12)}$$

In Experiment 16, these considerations are used for calculation of a neutron flux.

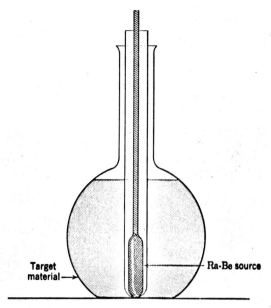

Figure 7. Experimental arrangement for Szilard-Chambers experiments, with liquid targets.

For the Szilard-Chalmers irradiations, the experimental arrangement in Figure 7 should be used. Since Pyrex glass contains boron, which has a cross section of approximately 4000 barns to thermal neutron capture, it is better to use a soft glass tube to hold the source.

EXPERIMENT 16

Neutron Flux Determination

Purpose:

To study the use of indium foils to measure a neutron flux.

Method:

(1) Obtain 4 indium foils of a proper size for insertion in the neutron source. Carefully weigh and determine the area of the foils. Foils of 50–100 mg per cm^2 are recommended. Irradiate the foils successively in identical fashion for periods of 30 min, 60 min, 120 min, and overnight (at least

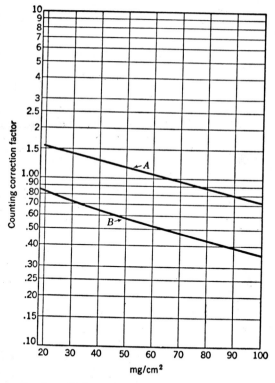

Figure 8. *A*—self-absorption, backscattering, and photon-contribution correction factor for Geiger-Müller counter at 2.2 cm from foils on thick Ag backing. *B*—same for 2π proportional-flow counter with foils on thick Ag backing. [*Nucleonics*, **15,** 57 (March, 1957) Figs. 3 and 5]

8 hours). After removal of each foil from the irradiator, wait several minutes to allow the In^{116g} ($t_{1/2} = 13$ sec) to decay out, then count the foil with a Geiger-Müller or a proportional counter every 15 minutes for a period of 1.5–2 hours. For all samples, begin the initial count the same period of time after removal of the foils from the irradiator.

(2) After an interval of at least 12 hours, wrap the foil which has been irradiated for 120 minutes with a piece of cadmium foil 0.020 inches thick and irradiate it and count it in exactly the same manner and for exactly the same time as before. It is very important that careful attention be paid to duplication of all details of irradiation and counting for the foils if valid results are to be obtained.

Data:

(1) Plot the cpm of In^{116m} per 100 mg of indium as a function of irradiation time. Use the initial count of each foil. From the decay curve, determine the half life for In^{116m}. Use the decay curves to check on the radiochemical purity of the foils.

(2) Determine the activity of the bare and the cadmium wrapped foil at the end of the bombardment by extrapolation of the observed decay curves from the initial count back to the time of removal of the foils from the neutron irradiator. Determine the value of C.R. and then, $A_{th}(x)$ using Equation (VIII-11) where $A(x)$ is the extrapolated activity of the bare foil. Use Figure 8 to estimate as accurately as possible $A_{th}(x)$ in disintegrations per minute. After correction to $A_{th}(0)$ by Equation (VIII-12), calculate the thermal flux by using Equation (VIII-6b) ($\sigma_{th} = 145$ barns). Calculate the ratio of thermal to epithermal induced activity, $A_{th}(0)/A_{epi}(0)$, from Equation (VIII-10). The references to Greenfield, et al., given in the text of this chapter should be consulted for this experiment.

EXPERIMENT 17

Neutron Activation of Silver

Purpose:

To calculate the activation cross section for silver.

Method:

Place a weighed piece of silver metal foil in the neutron source holder and irradiate for 10–12 minutes. A dime may be used for this experiment. It is necessary to work in pairs for this experiment.

One partner should prepare the Geiger-Müller (or proportional) counter for immediate operation when the silver sample is brought to the counter by the other partner. After positioning the sample, turn the counter on and, without interrupting the count, observe and record the total count registered every 10 seconds for the first 2 minutes, then every 30 seconds for the next 8 minutes. One partner should watch the time while the other watches the scaler registers for the total count.

If a count rate meter and recorder are available, they may be used with a Geiger-Müller tube. Have the count rate meter set for the medium time constant in the 5000 or 10,000 cpm range. One partner should turn the count rate meter on and have it registering about 4000 cpm by using a prepared source. When the silver sample is brought, replace the prepared source with the silver sample under the Geiger-Müller tube and start the recorder. The rate of paper movement in the recorder should be at least 1 inch per minute, and preferably more. When the count rate meter shows the rate to be below 1000 cpm, switch to the 1000 cpm scale, mark the position on the recorder trace and continue counting for a total time of 12–15 minutes.

Record the time from removal of the sample from the irradiator to initiation of the counting. Take background count determinations also. It may be necessary to repeat this experiment several times before practice gives the partners the degree of coordination necessary for obtaining reliable data.

Data:

Tabulate the counts recorded in each 10 sec time interval for the first 2 minutes and in each 30 sec time interval over the total counting time. Plot the activity vs. time on a semi-log scale and resolve the curve into two components. It may be necessary to make two graphs, one for the 10 sec and one for the 30 sec intervals. Determine the half lives and compare with those of Ag^{108} (2.3 min) and Ag^{110g} (24 sec).

Estimate the activity of Ag^{108} in dpm at the end of the irradiation by extrapolation of the decay curve back to that time and estimation of counting factors. Using the flux determination of Experiment 16, calculate the activation cross section for silver from Equation (VIII-7).

EXPERIMENT 18

Szilard-Chalmers Reaction (*I*)

Purpose:

To demonstrate the use of the Szilard-Chalmers reaction to prepare tracers of high specific activity which are isotopic with the target.

Method:

(1) *Irradiation of Ethyl Iodide.* Place approximately 200 ml of ethyl iodide containing a few milligrams of I_2 (added to act as carrier for the I^{128} formed) in a florence or Erlenmeyer flask. Place in the flask a large soft glass tube long enough to reach above the mouth of the flask. Insert the Ra-Be source in this flask and irradiate for an hour. *N.B.* Do not use a Pyrex test tube as the boron has a high capture cross section for thermal neutrons.

(2) *Separation of I^{128}.* Separate 100 ml of the irradiated ethyl iodide into two 50 ml samples (A and B). Record this as zero time. *Sample A.* Add 5 ml of distilled water, shake for several minutes in a separatory funnel and remove the aqueous layer into a test tube. Repeat with another 5 ml sample of water. Take caution in these extractions to relieve the pressure in the separatory funnel into a tissue. Add 1 ml of 0.1 N KI and 1 ml of 0.1 N HNO_3 solutions to the test tube solution, then precipitate AgI by addition of excess 1 N $AgNO_3$ solution. Filter the AgI precipitate and mount it for Geiger-Müller counting. Count the precipitate noting the elapsed time from when the separation began. *Sample B.* Add 5 ml of distilled water and 1 drop of Na_2SO_3 solution and extract as before. If the ethyl iodide does not decolorize completely, add another drop of Na_2SO_3. Remove the aqueous layer into a small beaker, add 2 ml of 1 N HNO_3 and boil gently with stirring for a couple of minutes. Wash quantitatively into a tube with a minimum of water, add 1 ml 0.1 N KI and precipitate as AgI with $AgNO_3$. Prepare a counting sample as before. Again, note the time of the initial count from zero. Place 5 ml of the original, irradiated ethyl iodide solution in a test tube and hydrolyze the ethyl iodide by adding 1 ml of concentrated HCl and warming. Then precipitate the total halide content of the tube with $AgNO_3$ and filter the silver halide. Mount the precipitate and count with the Geiger-Müller counter.

Follow the decay of the iodine activity by counting the AgI sample from B every 5 minutes for 40 to 50 minutes.

If a well scintillation counter is available, in 3 separate test tubes take 5 ml of the original ethyl iodide solution, the ethyl iodide after extraction in A, and after extraction in B. Count all three directly in the well scintillation counter.

Data:

Discuss the difference in extraction yield in A and B. What would have been the yield if no I_2 had been present during irradiation and why? Determine the half life of I^{128} from your data. Calculate the retention of I^{128} in the organic phase.

EXPERIMENT 19

Szilard-Chalmers Reaction (II)

Purpose:

To use isomeric transitions to prepare carrier free activities.

Method:

(1) Irradiate for an overnight period 200 ml of ethylene dibromide (or ethyl bromide) in the same fashion as Experiment 18. To 100 ml of the ethylene dibromide in a separatory funnel, add 10 ml of a solution 0.1 N in NaBr and 0.02 N in $NaHSO_3$ and shake for several minutes, periodically relieving the pressure in the separatory funnel by cautiously opening it with a tissue over the end to prevent spraying. Repeat this extraction, combine the two aqueous layers, and add 1 ml of 0.1 N HNO_3. Precipitate silver bromide by addition of excess $AgNO_3$ solution. Heat to coagulate, filter, wash with water and acetone, air dry, then mount for Geiger-Müller counting. Follow the half life of this sample for four hours, counting every 5 minutes for the first half hour.

(2) Two hours after the initial separation, repeat the procedure and follow the half life of this second sample.

Data:

Explain the difference in the two half life curves and account for the activity seen in the second sample.

EXPERIMENT 20

Szilard-Chalmers Reaction (III)

Purpose:

To study the use of Szilard-Chalmers reaction in an inorganic system.

Method:

(1) After preparation of a concentrated solution of either $NaMnO_4$ or $Ca(MnO_4)_2$ (50 grams per 100 ml of distilled water), filter it through a sintered glass funnel.

Determine the concentration of this solution by titration of I_3^- with 0.1 M $Na_2S_2O_3$ and starch indicator, using the disappearance of the color as

the end point. The sample to be titrated is prepared by addition of a 200 microliter aliquot of the filtered permanganate solution to a solution of 2 grams of KI, 20 ml of distilled water and 4 ml concentrated HCl. After standing in the dark for three minutes, the sample is diluted to 100 ml and the titration performed.

(2) Place 100–200 ml of permanganate solution in an Erlenmeyer flask and irradiate overnight in the same manner as the ethyl iodide sample in Experiment 16.

After irradiation, remove 100 ml of solution and filter the solution through a piece of Whatman No. 50 filter paper using the usual filter assembly. Wash the precipitate with distilled water until all the permanganate color is removed, then with acetone. Air dry the filter paper before mounting it in a standard fashion for precipitates for Geiger-Müller counting. Follow the count rate over several hours to determine the half life of the Mn^{56}.

Place 5 ml of the unfiltered irradiated solution and 5 ml of the filtrate in test tubes and count in a well scintillation counter. If there is no well counter available, prepare solid samples for Geiger-Müller counting by evaporation to near dryness, then after quantitative transfer to a stainless steel cup planchet, evaporation to dryness.

Data:

Compare the count rate of the two samples to obtain a retention factor for the Mn^{56} in permanganate solution.

PROBLEMS

1. For production of the following nuclides, choose and explain the basis for the choice between cyclotron irradiation, neutron activation and fission.

$$Cs^{137} \quad Hg^{197} \quad Pm^{147} \quad Cl^{36}$$
$$Co^{60} \quad C^{14} \quad S^{35} \quad Co^{58}$$

2. In a flux of 10^{13} neutrons per cm^2 per sec, how long an irradiation is necessary to reduce the amount of W^{186} ($\sigma = 37$ barns) present in tungsten foil by 10%?

3. For a flux of 10^{13} $n/cm^2/s$ and a 1 gm sample of $KMnO_4$, calculate the activity of Mn^{56} which will be formed after an irradiation of (a) 15 minutes, (b) 90 minutes, (c) 200 minutes. Calculate the activities for each time by Equations (VIII-6), (VIII-7), and (VIII-8a) and compare.

4. What per cent of the total activity in a 1 gram sample of gold foil will be due to Au^{199} following a 1.5 day irradiation with a flux of 10^{14} $n/cm^2/s$ [$\sigma_{197} = 96$ b; $\sigma_{198} = 35000$ b; $t_{1/2}(198) = 2.7$ d; $t_{1/2}(199) = 3.15$ d]?

5. For a Szilard-Chalmers reaction, a 100 gram ethyl iodide sample was irradiated with a neutron flux of 2×10^4 $n/cm^2/s$ for an hour. If there is a 20% retention and separation occurs 5 minutes after the end of irradiation, what will be the activity of the AgI sample (in dpm) 10 minutes after separation?

6. Ignoring any possible resonance peaks, if the cross section of B^{10} for thermal (0.025 ev) neutrons is 3990 barns, construct the cross section vs. neutron energy plot from 0.025 ev to 100 ev.

7. A linear accelerator with protons whose initial energy is 32 Mev is available for bombardments. It is desired to prepare Zn^{62} tracer by the reaction

$$Cu^{63}\ (p,\ 2n)\ Zn^{62}$$

Calculate the amount that can be made with a 1 hour bombardment of a thin target of 1.0 mg of copper by a beam of protons whose intensity is 50 microamperes and whose energy is 32 Mev.

8. What proton energy should be used for maximum yield in Problem **7**? Use Figure 3, Chapter III to determine the thickness of Al foil necessary to degrade the beam energy to this value from the initial 32 Mev.

9. Outline a method of separation of the Zn^{62} from the target in Problem **7** so that it may be isolated in a radiochemically pure form.

10. Assuming it is necessary to observe a minimum of 700 dpm, what is the lower limit on the amount of indium impurity that could be detected in a 100 mg sample of aluminum with a thermal neutron flux of $10^{12}\ n/cm^2/s$?

REFERENCES

Friedlander, G., and J. W. Kennedy, *Nuclear and Radiochemistry.* New York: John Wiley & Sons, Inc., 1955, Chapter 4.

Hughes, D. J., and J. A. Harvey, *Neutron Cross Sections* (U. S. A. E. C. Document). New York: McGraw-Hill Book Co., Inc., 1955.

Lapp, R. E., and H. L. Andrews, *Nuclear Radiation Physics.* Englewood Cliffs, N. J.: Prentice-Hall, Inc., 1954, Chapter 4.

McKay, H. A. C., *Progress in Nuclear Chemistry.* New York: Academic Press, 1950, Vol. 1.

Williams, R. R., *Principles of Nuclear Chemistry.* New York: D. Van Nostrand Co., 1950, Chapter VII.

Williams, Hamil, and Schuler, *J. Chem. Educ.*, **26**, 210, 310, 667 (1949).

Activation Analysis

Guinn, V. P., and C. D. Wagner, *Anal. Chem.*, **32**, 317 (1960).

Jenkins, E. N., and A. A. Smales, *Quart. Rev. Chem. Soc.* (London), **10** (1956), 83.

Meinke, W. W., *Anal. Chem.*, **31**, 792 (1959).

Plumb, R. C., *Nucleonics*, **14**, 48 (May, 1956).

IX

Separation Techniques

THE basic methods used in the purification of radioactive samples are those of analytical chemistry. However, a few important differences exist in the requirements of radiochemical purification necessitating some modification of the basic analytical techniques. First, radiochemical purity is frequently of greater importance than chemical purity; it may be better to have a milligram of inert impurity in the final sample than 10^{-9} gm of radioactive contaminant. The tolerance for the two types of impurities is determined by the particular experiment involved. For example, usually much greater radiochemical contamination is allowable if gamma scintillation spectrometry is to be used for counting, rather than Geiger-Müller counting. In contrast, if a chemical yield must be determined for the separation of a 10 mg sample, the chemical impurities must be well below the milligram level.

Secondly, speed may be more important than a high chemical yield or even great radiochemical purity. Obviously a very clean, high yield separation scheme which requires an hour to perform is of no interest for isolating and studying a nuclide with a 5 minute half life. Furthermore, the intensity of the radioactivity may require operation by remote control. Even if the level of activity does not make it necessary, the volumes are best kept to a minimum to allow semi-microchemical operations for better control of the activity. For all these reasons simple, efficient separations are favored even at the expense of quantitative yield.

Precipitation

The preparation of a final counting sample of a radioactive substance usually requires deposition in some fashion on a backing material. One of the most common methods for such deposition utilizes precipitation of an insoluble compound which carries with it the active species. If knowledge of the yield is important, the usual procedure is to add, prior to any chemical separations, a known amount of a stable substance isotopic with the active species. Determination with an analytical balance of the weight of the final precipitate allows evaluation of the over-all yield. It is necessary that the precipitate meet the normal requirements of a gravimetric determination, except that of quantitative insolubility. The precipitate should be easily filtered and free of impurities, both in a macro and a radiochemical sense. The stoichiometric composition of the final, dried sample must be well known, and it should not absorb moisture or CO_2. For beta counting it must be of relatively thin, uniform thickness.

Before the final precipitation, a separation scheme may include several other precipitation steps designed to increase radiochemical purity. The requirements are not as critical for these intermediate precipitates but optimum freedom from contaminants is desirable. To achieve this, certain procedures for precipitation should be followed. First, relatively dilute solutions of the reagents should be used and the precipitating reagent slowly added to a hot solution. The pH of the solutions should be chosen to minimize colloid formation and surface adsorption on the precipitate. Digestion of the precipitate helps to remove adsorbed or trapped impurities. In washing, care must be taken not to peptize the precipitate. To remove contaminants further, the precipitate may be dissolved and reprecipitated. This process is recommended for amorphous precipitates of very large surface areas, such as the hydrous oxides. In these precipitates even extensive washing fails to remove completely the adsorbed ions such as Na^+ or Cl^-, whereas quantitative removal may be accomplished by one or two reprecipitations. Colloid formation is to be avoided, as it allows some or all of the desired activity to pass through the filter, and the great surface area results in high adsorption of impurities which are carried down with the precipitate upon flocculation.

At times it may not be possible or desirable to precipitate the radioactivity of interest with a macro amount of an inactive isotopic carrier. For Tc, Pm, and the elements above bismuth, no inactive isotopes are available. For preparation of sources of low energy beta emitters, a carrier free preparation is very desirable as it minimizes absorption and attenua-

tion. In these cases purification is often accomplished by coprecipitation with a non-isotopic carrier. Two modes of coprecipitation are important: mixed crystal formation and adsorption. The techniques described earlier for precipitation do not affect the extent of coprecipitation by mixed crystal formation but do decrease it by adsorption.

If the active ion would form a compound with the oppositely charged ion of the precipitate which, in macro amounts, would be isomorphous with the precipitate, the active ion may be included in the crystal lattice of the precipitate at a lattice point. This mixed crystal formation is favored if the active ion is close in size to the ion which it displaces. However, exceptions both to this and the requirement of isomorphism are found, especially at tracer level concentrations. If the distribution of the tracer is found to be uniform throughout the precipitate, the homogeneous (or Berthelot-Nernst) distribution law has been followed. This law is the same as that for the distribution of a solute between two liquid phases and is given by

$$\frac{x}{y} = D\left[\frac{a - x}{b - y}\right] \qquad \text{(IX-1)}$$

where x and y are the amounts of A^+ and B^+ in the precipitate, a and b the initial amounts of A^+ and B^+, and D the distribution coefficient. The entire precipitate is in equilibrium with the solution in this system.

If only the freshly forming surface of the growing crystal is in equilibrium with the solution phase, then a logarithmic (Doerner-Hoskins) distribution law describes the system. The equation is

$$\ln\left[\frac{a}{a - x}\right] = \Lambda \ln\left[\frac{b}{b - y}\right] \qquad \text{(IX-2)}$$

where Λ is the distribution coefficient. The activity is not uniformly distributed throughout the precipitate. Moderately slow evaporation of a solution to form a precipitate with large crystals favors this non-uniform distribution as it allows the growing surface to be in equilibrium with the solution but does not allow the deeper layers to re-equilibrate. If a finely divided precipitate is digested—allowing extensive recrystallization—homogeneous distribution is more likely. Of course, these represent limiting laws and the distribution is frequently between these extremes.

Adsorption on precipitate surfaces is important at tracer concentrations because the fraction of the amount of a solute adsorbed increases as the concentration decreases. The amount of adsorption depends on the area and the nature of the surface. If the activity is attracted to the surface by electrical attraction and forms an insoluble compound with its counter ion in the precipitate, adsorption is favored. The surface charge often may be reversed in sign by changing the pH or by adding proper electrolytes, thus reducing adsorption. Frequently, holdback carriers are added prior to a precipitation. These are isotopic with activities which it is desired not to coprecipitate and reduce adsorption of the active species by decreasing the fraction adsorbed simply through a mass effect. Holdback carriers may be used to minimize radiochemical contamination of a precipitate of interest or to minimize loss of activity on a precipitate removing contaminants.

Experimental

Examples of coprecipitation have been met in Experiments 7 and 12. The method of filtration was discussed in Chapter V.

EXPERIMENT 21

Isotopic Precipitation

Purpose:

To study a short-lived nuclide after isolation by precipitation.

Method:

In this experiment a barium isotope of less than three minute half life is to be isolated, so speed is necessary. Prepare a filter assembly for use. Also, carefully plan the procedure so no interruptions to obtain or set up equipment will be necessary. Practice the procedure at least twice without using active material.

(1) Pipet approximately 10,000 cpm of Cs^{137} activity into a small test tube containing a 0.1 N HNO_3 solution with 1 mg Ba^{++}. Mix thoroughly and then, noting the exact time, add 100 microliters of a 0.5 N Na_2SO_4 solution. Stir rapidly with a glass rod, then pour the solution through the filter assembly, catching the filtrate in another test tube, again recording the time of completion of the filtration. Wash with 0.1 ml aliquots of water, alcohol, and acetone, disassemble the filter setup and dry the filter paper and precipitate of $BaSO_4$ under an infrared heat lamp in the hood. Then lay the filter paper on a piece of Scotch Tape and affix it to a sample holder, covering it with cellophane as in Experiment 4.

Place the sample in the NaI scintillation counter and record the time when the count is begun. Take readings every 30 seconds without turning the counter off, one partner reading the scalar, the other keeping the data. Follow the sample for ten minutes, then remove and take a background. If a scintillation counter is not available, use a Geiger-Müller counter.

(2) Prepare a Cs^{137} sample of the same quantity used in the precipitation and count in the NaI counter.

(3) Prepare the filter assembly again. To the filtrate from (1) add a

sufficient amount of Ba^{++} solution to have 1 mg of Ba^{++}. Note the exact time of the addition and stir rapidly during the addition. Again, follow filtering and counting procedure as in (1).

Data:

Extrapolate the Ba^{137m} decay curves back to the mean filtration time and compare the cpm in 1, 2, and 3. Show the decay scheme in your report for Cs^{137} and Ba^{137m}. Discuss the comparison in count rate in 1, 2, and 3. The mean filtration time is used rather than the time of initial precipitation because the exchange between Ba^{++} and $BaSO_4$ is very rapid so that much of the Ba^{137m} formed between the time of precipitation and filtration will also be incorporated in the precipitate.

EXPERIMENT 22

Coprecipitation

Purpose:

To study the non-isotopic carrying of radioactive substances under various conditions.

Method:

Prepare solutions of Ag^+ (10 mg per ml), Tl^+ (10 mg per ml), HCl (0.1 N), NaOH (0.1 N) and Tl^{204} tracer solution of about 10,000 cpm per 50 microliters when counted by either a proportional or a Geiger-Müller counter.

(1) Place 2 drops of 0.1 N HCl on a counting disc, add 50 microliters of tracer and evaporate to dryness; use the same type of counting planchet in all these experiments. They must be capable of holding up to 0.5 ml of solution. Cover the planchet with a thin plastic foil such as Saran before counting.

(2) *Carrying on AgCl, carrier free.* To a centrifuge cone add 2 drops of Ag^+ solution, 50 microliters of tracer and 5 drops of water. Add 3 drops of 0.1 N HCl to cause precipitation. Stir and centrifuge, then test for completeness of precipitation by addition of another drop of HCl to the supernatant liquid. If incomplete, recentrifuge and again test. When the precipitation is complete, carefully remove as much of the supernate as possible with a transfer pipet and place on a planchet. *Be careful not to transfer any precipitate to the planchet.* Dry and count.

(3) *Carrying on AgCl, carrier present.* Repeat the procedure, outlined above, adding a drop of the Tl^+ carrier solution after adding the Tl^{204} tracer.

(4) *Carrying on preformed AgCl, carrier free, excess Cl^-.* To a cone add

2 drops of Ag⁺ solution and 6 drops of 0.1 N HCl, then 50 microliters of tracer. Stir for several minutes, centrifuge and prepare the supernate for counting.

(5) *Carrying on preformed AgCl, carrier present, excess Cl⁻.* In one cone mix 50 microliters of tracer and 1 drop of Tl^+ carrier and enough water to make about $\frac{3}{4}$ ml. In a second cone mix 2 drops of Ag⁺ solution and 6 drops of HCl as in (4) to prepare an AgCl suspension. Pour the contents of the second cone into the first and stir for a few minutes. Centrifuge and prepare the supernate as before. Because of the greater volume, necessary to make sure that the solubility of TlCl is not exceeded, it may be necessary to evaporate the supernate by several additions to the planchet.

(6) *Carrying on preformed AgCl, carrier free, excess Ag⁺.* Prepare an AgCl suspension from 6 drops of Ag⁺ solution and 2 drops of 0.1 N HCl, then proceed as in (4).

(7) *Carrying on preformed AgCl, carrier present, excess Ag⁺.* In one cone mix 50 microliters of tracer, 1 drop of Tl^+ carrier and a few drops of water. In a second cone, make an AgCl suspension as in (6) and proceed as in (5).

(8) *Carrying on Ag_2O, carrier free.* Mix 2 drops of Ag⁺, 50 microliters of tracer and a few drops of water. Then, add a drop of NaOH, centrifuge, and prepare supernate for counting.

(9) *Carrying on Ag_2O, carrier present.* Repeat (8), adding a drop of Tl^+ carrier solution before the NaOH.

Data:

Calculate the per cent carried in each experiment and discuss the meaning of these results.

Electrodeposition

In addition to its application in separation schemes, electrodeposition is used in the preparation of accelerator targets and of thin, standard counting samples. Radioactive sources for use in alpha and beta spectroscopy are prepared frequently by electrodeposition techniques, as the uniform nature of the deposit minimizes attenuation effects.

With electrolysis, two techniques of electrodeposition are employed. In the first, metals are deposited on the cathode from solutions of their ions. Cu, Co, Ni are some of the elements which may be isolated in this fashion. In the second technique, the cationic species is precipitated in an insoluble form on the electrode. Many elements have too large an oxidation potential to be deposited in the metallic state in aqueous solutions but can be deposited by this second method. For example, the lanthanide and actinide elements in the region of high pH adjacent to a cathode surface, precipitate as the hydrous oxides, even in trace quantities. The rate of deposition is dependent on the extent of the zone of high pH, which is a function of the current density of the cathode. Solutions of ammonium

salts (pH 3) are used and it is necessary to neutralize the solution with NH_4OH before terminating electrolysis to prevent dissolution of the cathodic precipitate. It is possible to deposit UF_4 on a cathode from $(NH_4)_2SiF_6$ solution in similar fashion.

In separation methods, electrochemical displacement is used in some cases. For example, Po is separable from Pb by deposition on a piece of silver foil or wire. Bi may be separated from a lead target after dissolution by deposition on Ni powder from hot $0.5\ N$ HCl solution. For the theory of electrochemical deposition or replacement, any basic physical chemistry text may be consulted.

Experimental

A simple electroplating cell may be prepared as in Figure 1. A piece of glass tubing of 1 cm diameter and 6 cm length is ground level at one end and glass ears affixed near the opposite end. The cell is assembled by placing a piece of aluminum foil on a square of lucite (some other plastic, wood, or metal will serve, also), then placing a metal disc on this and finally adding the glass chimney, with the ground end down. Use rubber bands to hold the assembly together and spread around the outside a thin layer of Duco or Lepage cement to seal the chimney and disc together. Allow about 30 minutes drying time for the cement before use. The aluminum foil should have a projection for attachment of an alligator clip lead from the power supply. A Heathkit Battery Eliminator, Model BE-5 or suitable batteries (e.g., Eveready Hobby Batteries) provide adequate power sources.

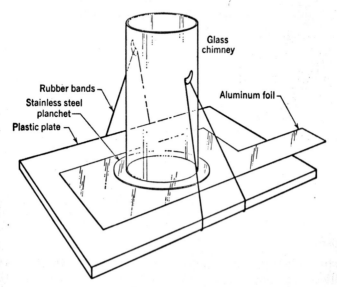

Figure 1. Experimental arrangement for electrodeposition.

EXPERIMENT 23

Electrodeposition of Cobalt

Purpose:

To study an example of sample preparation by metal electrodeposition.

Method:

Prepare a solution of $(NH_4)_2SO_4$(50% sat'd.). Assemble the electrolysis cell using a platinum or stainless steel disc as the cathode. Attach a lead to the Al foil so that it will function as the cathode. For the anode, suspend a piece of coiled Pt wire into the solution. Place 10 ml of the $(NH_4)_2SO_4$ solution into the cell, add 1 ml of a $CoSO_4$ solution of 1 mg Co^{++} per ml and sufficient tracer solution to have 10,000 cpm of Co^{60}. Begin the electrolysis and run for 5 minutes at 2.5 ma current. Prepare 3 other cells with the same solution. At the end of 5 minutes, remove the anode, then turn off the current. Pour the liquid into an active waste jar and wash the disc with H_2O, alcohol, and acetone, discarding all wash liquid in the same jar. Dry the disc under a heat lamp, then count in a Geiger-Müller or proportional counter.

Repeat the electrolysis with the other samples for 15, 30, and 60 minute intervals at 2.5 ma. Also prepare a Co^{60} sample of the same aliquot on a stainless steel disc and count after drying. Weigh the cathode discs from the electroplating to get the weight of Co deposited. Be careful that the voltage is insufficient to cause evolution of H_2.

Data:

Plot %Co electroplated vs. time for both the counting data and the weighing data. Calculate the weight of Co which should have been deposited in each time interval according to Faraday's Law, and plot this also on the same graph. Discuss sources of discrepancy thoroughly.

EXPERIMENT 24

Electrodeposition of Uranium

Purpose:

To study the technique of preparation of counting standards by electrodeposition of thin uniform films. Uranium is precipitated as $U(OH)_4$ in the cathode area after reduction from UO_2^{2+}.

Method:

This method is adapted from that of Hufford and Scott (Paper 16.1, Vol. 14B, National Nuclear Energy Series, New York: McGraw-Hill Book Co., Inc.). The electrolysis cell is prepared as described with a platinum or stainless steel disc previously weighed on a semi-micro analytical balance. The anode consists of a coiled platinum wire, rotating at 500 rpm (however, it is not absolutely necessary that the anode be rotated). A volume of 0.4 M ammonium oxalate solution of pH 3.5 such that there is at least 1.5 ml of solution per square cm of cathode surface is added to the cell assembly. The solution also contains a sufficient concentration of $UO_2(NO_3)_2$ that with 100% deposition efficiency, 0.5 mg of U_3O_8 per square cm of cathode surface would be obtained. The electrolysis is carried out at a current density of 0.15 amp per square cm for 50 minutes. If the current drops during this time, add a few small crystals of ammonium oxalate to the solution. Before the current is turned off, ammonium hydroxide is added to prevent acid solution of the $U(OH)_4$ deposit. Lower the cell to remove the anode from the solution before turning off the current, then disassemble the cell and rinse the cathode with water, alcohol, and acetone. After drying, the deposit is ignited gently over a flame to form U_3O_8. Also prepare a sample of a 0.5 ml aliquot of the solution directly on a counting disc, evaporate and flame.

Data:

Examine the deposit visually for uniformity. Count and weigh the disc and calculate the efficiency of the electrode position. If possible, use a proportional counter set for the alpha plateau.

Ion Exchange

Two techniques of major importance in separation schemes are ion exchange and solvent extraction. An ion exchanger consists of a three-dimensional polymeric matrix throughout which are affixed either cationic or anionic functional groups. If the functional group is anionic, the exchange occurs between the counter cations and the material is designated as a cation exchanger. Anion exchangers, conversely, possess cationic groups and so exchange anions. To be of practical value as an ion exchange material, the matrix network must be sufficiently open to allow relatively free diffusion of the counter ions. Although many natural clay minerals and synthetic inorganic substances possess ion exchange properties, the synthetic organic resins are much more widely used.

The most commonly used strong acid cation exchange resin is prepared by sulfonating polystyrene. The resulting structure is shown in Figure 2. The amount of cross linking is controlled by the proportion of divinyl benzene to styrene in the polymerization process. These sulfonic acid resins are available commercially in bead form in a wide variety of mesh sizes and cross linkages. The principal sulfonic acid resins are Dowex-50 (Dow Chemical Co.) and Amberlite-IR-120 (Rohm and Haas Co.). Weak acid cation exchange resins are available also with carboxyl groups attached to the rings.

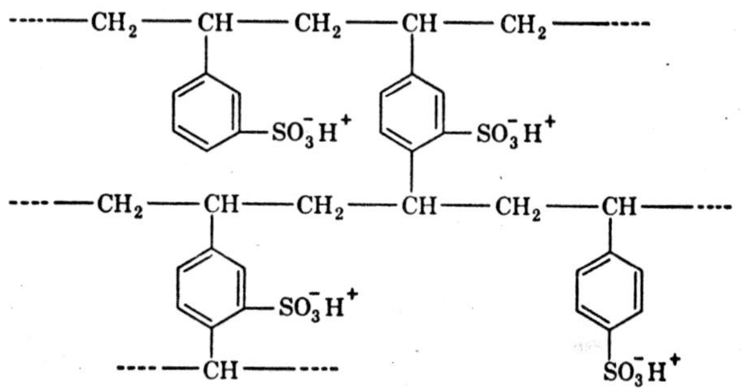

Figure 2. The type of structure present in a typical strong acid cation exchange resin, for example, Dowex-50.

A quaternary ammonium polystyrene resin known as Dowex-1 (also, Amberlite-IRA-400) is a strong base anion exchanger. Secondary and tertiary amine resins act as weaker base exchangers.

Thermodynamics of Ion Exchange

If a cation exchange resin with A^+ present is contacted with a solution containing B^+ ions, the following ion exchange equilibrium is set up:

$$AR + B^+ \rightleftharpoons BR + A^+ \qquad \text{(IX-3)}$$

where AR and BR represent the ions in the resin phase and A^+ and B^+ the ions in the solution phase. The concentration equilibrium quotient is

$$K_c = \frac{[BR]\,[A^+]}{[AR]\,[B^+]} \qquad \text{(IX-4)}$$

Even when $[A^+] = [B^+]$, K_c is rarely unity. This fact, indicating a greater preference by the resin phase for one of the ions, is of prime importance in ion exchange. Although a number of theories have been advanced for the selectivity of resins, none are sufficiently complete to allow accurate a priori calculation of selectivities.

The thermodynamically valid equilibrium constant K_e requires the use of activities rather than concentrations, so that

$$K_e = K_c\left(\frac{\gamma_{BR}}{\gamma_{AR}} \times \frac{\gamma_A}{\gamma_B}\right) \qquad \text{(IX-5)}$$

Application of the Donnan membrane theory to these systems leads to the expression

$$\frac{a_{BR}}{a_{AR}} = \frac{a_B}{a_A}$$

where the a terms represent the activities. Using this expression, it is possible to rewrite Equation (IX-4) as

$$\frac{[AR][B]}{[BR][A]} = \frac{\gamma_{BR}}{\gamma_{AR}}\frac{\gamma_A}{\gamma_B} = \frac{1}{K_c} \tag{IX-6}$$

Since in dilute solutions $\gamma_A \approx \gamma_B$, the selectivity would seem to be largely due to the difference in activity coefficients of the two cations in the resin phase. This phase may be treated as a concentrated electrolyte solution (2–6 molal). However, use of γ_A/γ_B ratios from salt solutions of this concentration is only a first approximation as it assumes no perturbation due to the extensive organic matrix present in the resin phase. Qualitative correlation is obtained with experimental selectivities, but quantitative agreement must await development of an adequate theory of concentrated electrolyte solutions. In highly cross-linked resins, it is also necessary to take into account an internal swelling pressure due to the stretching of the polymer network as a result of water absorption. These considerations will be valid for anion exchange also.

Some general observations may be made on the relative order of selectivity for cation resins:

(A) In dilute solutions the order of resin attraction is the same as the lyotrophic series which is the order of the hydrated radius (the inverse order of the crystallographic radius). In the alkali metals, this predicts the order to be

$$Li^+ < Na^+ < K^+ < Rb^+ < Cs^+$$

Li$^+$ has the lowest attraction to the resin phase as it has the largest hydrated radius.

(B) The attraction to the resin phase increases with valency in dilute solutions.

$$Na^+ < Ca^{+2} < Al^{+3} < Th^{+4}$$

(C) In concentrated solutions, and at high temperatures, the selectivity may decrease or the above order may even reverse.

(D) Selectivity increases as the amount of cross linking increases.

Kinetics of Ion Exchange

In elutions of ions from ion exchange resin columns, the efficiency of separation depends on the rate of flow of eluting solution through the column. Since with the strong base and strong acid resins no covalent bonds need be broken, for solutions above 0.1 M concentration the diffusion of the counter ions through the resin particle is the rate controlling process. The resin particle size, the temperature, the solution concentration and the amount of hydration and cross-linkage of the resin are all factors in determining the rate at which elution may be performed under near-equilibrium conditions.

Applications

Ion exchange is of value to the user of radioactivity because it provides a technique for the rapid separation of similar ions in low concentrations. A description of ion exchange separations in terms of plate theory analogous to distillation plate theory indicates that even in very small resin beds, several thousand theoretical plates may be present. Thus, it is easy to understand the excellent separations obtained even when the difference in selectivities between ions is not large. This multistep separation process is one of the advantages that ion exchange possesses over solvent extraction systems in the separation of small amounts of active ions. The counter current distribution technique provides multistep separations by solvent extraction but this technique is frequently not adaptable to the use of the radiochemist. The ability to separate only a few atoms from relatively large amounts of non-isotopic material is one of the most desirable features of both ion exchange and solvent extraction.

Among the successes of the ion exchange technique has been the separation of Hf and Zr, of amino acids, and of the lanthanide and actinide elements. In the case of the latter, elution has been achieved by combining the complexing power of an anion with the exchange process. The reactions may be written as

$$La^{+3} + 3 NH_4^+R \rightleftharpoons LaR_3 + 3 NH_4^+ \qquad \text{(IX-7a)}$$

$$La^{+3} + nX^- \rightleftharpoons LaX_n^{3-n} \qquad \text{(IX-7b)}$$

The complex formation reduces the concentration of the La^{+3} ion and so serves to drive the resin equation to the left. Fortunately, the order of complex formation and that of resin selectivity are the same so the net effect is increased separation. Such systems have been used with active tracers to measure the complex formation constants. The complexing anions that have been used for the lanthanides and actinides include citrate, glycolate, lactate, and alpha-hydroxy isobutyrate.[1]

Kraus and co-workers at Oak Ridge National Laboratory have demonstrated the applicability of anion exchange resins in metal ion separations. The most extensively studied system is that of Dowex-1 and hydrochloric acid. Many metals form strong anionic complexes with chloride ion, others

[1] G. R. Choppin, "Ion Exchange Studies of the Actinide Elements," *J. Chem. Educ.*, **36**, 462 (1959).

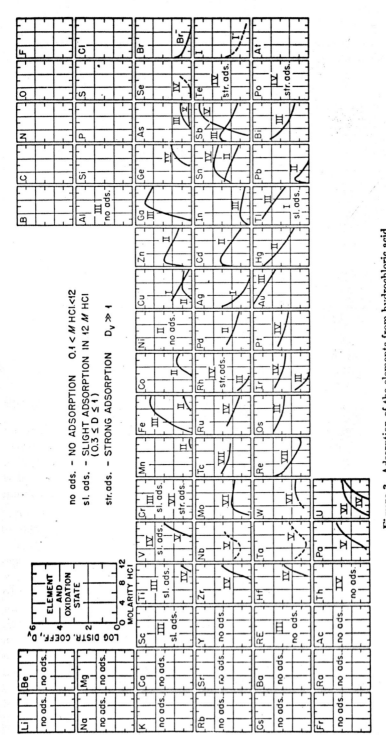

Figure 3. Adsorption of the elements from hydrochloric acid.
[Kraus and Nelson, *Paper* 837, Geneva Conference Vol. 7 (1956).]

141

form weaker anionic complexes and others form no complexes or only cationic ones. The exchange reaction for a metal M is

$$MCl_n^{-z} + xRCl \rightleftharpoons R_zMCl_n + xCl^-$$ (IX-8a)

In some cases neutral complexes are adsorbed by the reaction

$$MCl_m + RCl \rightleftharpoons RMCl_{m+1}$$ (IX-8b)

By choosing the proper concentration of hydrochloric acid, non- or poorly adsorbed ions may be eluted while more strongly adsorbed ions remain in the resin bed. The concentration of eluant may then be changed to cause elution of the latter ions, also, by driving Equation (IX-8) to the left. This is done if the Cl^- concentration increases sufficiently or if the MCl_n^{-z} concentration decreases due to dissociation of the complex at low HCl concentrations. Figure 3 is a résumé of the results of the Oak Ridge group.

The distribution coefficient, K_D, is defined as

$$K_D = \frac{[M](\text{resin})}{[M](\text{solution})}$$

$$= \frac{\text{cpm in resin phase per gm of resin}}{\text{cpm in solution phase per ml of solution}}$$ (IX-9)

The separation factor, α_B^A, for two ions relative to each other is given by

$$\alpha_B^A = \frac{K_{D(A)}}{K_{D(B)}} = \frac{V_A - a}{V_B - a}$$ (IX-10)

where V_A and V_B are the volumes of eluant which have passed when the maximum is reached in the elution curves of ion A and B, and a is a correction factor for the volume of solution in the resin bed when elution began. This volume may be assumed to be 40% of the total bed volume and is known as the free column volume. If n_A is the number of free column volumes in V_A, and n_B is the same for V_B then

$$\alpha_B^A = n_A - 1/n_B - 1$$

Experimental

The resin columns should be carefully prepared by adding the resin to the glass column in an aqueous slurry from a transfer pipet. The resin for these experiments should be −400 mesh and graded by settling in water. The fractions settling at 0.25–0.75 cm per min and 0.75–1.0 cm per min are recommended for optimum results. There should be no air or solution gaps in the resin bed and the solution volume below the resin bed should be held to a minimum. If the resin bed is allowed to go dry, air gaps may result and it is then necessary to repack the bed. Figure 4 shows a typical column.

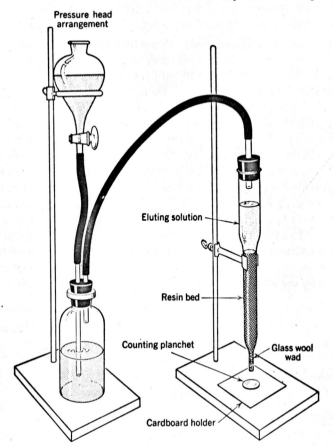

Figure 4. Ion exchange elution column and pressure head.

If necessary, pressure may be applied to the solution above the resin bed to increase the flow rate.

The student is referred to Experiment 11, Chapter VI for another separation technique using ion exchange resins.

EXPERIMENT 25

Separation of Alkali Metal Ions

Purpose:

To use Dowex-50 cation exchange resin to effect the separation of Na^{22} and Cs^{137}.

Method:

Prepare a cation exchange resin column by transferring an aqueous slurry of the resin (Dowex-50 4% cross-linked) to a glass column so that the resin bed measures 3 mm (I.D.) by 10 cm long. Then run at least 2 ml of 3 N hydrochloric acid through the bed. Do not allow the bed to go dry at any time.

Add about 2000 cpm each of Na^{22} and Cs^{137} to a drop of 3 M HCl on a glass counting disc, then evaporate to dryness. When the liquid level of 3 N HCl in the column reaches the top of the resin, add 1 drop of 3 N HCl to the disc, move it around gently to dissolve all of the Na and Cs, then transfer it to the top of the resin bed. Begin collecting the drops from the column on glass counting discs, 2 drops per plate. When the initial loading drop has run into the resin, rinse the space above the resin with another drop of acid and let this also run into the resin. Then add 3 ml of the 3 N acid and continue the elution until both bands of radioactivity have come off the resin. Evaporate the drops to dryness under a heat lamp and count the discs on the NaI(Tl) scintillation counter or the Geiger-Müller counter.

Data:

Plot cpm after subtraction of background versus plate number. Calculate the full width at half maximum for each peak and express this half width as the percentage of the total elution volume to the maximum of the peak. Identify the peaks from the energy of the gamma rays by use of the single channel analyzer or by Pb absorption.

Also, calculate the separation factor for Cs relative to Na. Use the equation

$$p = \frac{2n(n-1)}{W^2}$$

to calculate the effective number of theoretical plates (p). The number of free column volumes to the maximum in the elution peak is n, and W is the width at 0.368 of the maximum.

EXPERIMENT 26

Separation of Ce and Pr by Ion Exchange

Purpose:

To study the separation of rare earth ions by ion exchange.

Method:

Prepare a column with resin bed dimensions 2 mm (I.D.) by 5 cm (length) using Dowex-50 4% cross-linked. Also prepare 50 ml of a solution of 0.25 M

glycolic acid which has been adjusted with concentrated NH₄OH* to a
pH value of 4.2 ± 0.05 of a pH unit. Pass 3–4 ml of this solution through
the resin bed.

Place 3000 cpm of Ce¹⁴⁴ tracer on a glass disc and evaporate to dryness
under a heat lamp. Prior to loading the activity onto the resin remove
the glycolate solution from above the resin and rinse with water. Then,
pass 1 drop of H_2O and then, 1 drop of 0.1 N HCl through the resin. Load
the activity on the column in 1 drop of 0.1 N HCl (wash the glass disc as
well as possible with this one drop), then follow this on the resin with a
drop of H_2O and a drop of the glycolate solution. The purpose of this procedure is to transfer all the activity to the resin in the narrowest possible
band and to avoid having the activity diffuse into the solution above the
resin bed when the eluant is added. Begin catching the eluting drops on
numbered glass plates (2 per plate) when this last drop is placed on the
resin bed. Then add several ml of glycolate solution above the resin and
begin elution, running the elution at the rate of 1 drop per minute. Continue the elution until both the Ce and Pr have eluted.

Data:

Since the Pr¹⁴⁴ has a 17 min half life, it is important to count the drops
soon after elution. Identify the peaks by following the decay (or growth)
of radioactivity in the plate of each peak with the maximum radioactivity.
From the initial counts, plot cpm versus plate number. Calculate the half
width (i.e., full width at half maximum) for each peak and the separation
factor for Ce and Pr.

EXPERIMENT 27

Anion Exchange Resin Separation

Purpose:

To use anion exchange resin to separate U²³⁸, Pa²³⁴ and Th²³⁴.

Method:

Prepare an anion resin column by adding an aqueous slurry of anion
resin to the column. The final resin bed dimensions should be 4 mm I.D.
and 8 cm long. Pass 2 ml of 10 N HCl through the column to convert the
resin to the chloride form.

Prepare a solution which is 0.2 M in U(VI) and 10 N in HCl. To ensure

---

* It may be necessary to change these concentration and pH conditions slightly as
different batches of resin have different K_D values. It is desirable to have the cerium
(the second) peak reach its maximum at about plate 10–12 (drops 20–25).

that the uranium remains in the hexavalent state, add a drop of hydrogen peroxide per ml of solution. Transfer 200 microliters of this solution to the column and collect the eluant on stainless steel counting discs (2 drops per plate). Wash the column with two 100 microliter samples of 10 N HCl, allowing each to run in the resin before adding the next. Then add 10 drops of 10 N HCl. Dry the plates after collecting the second drop and count in a Geiger-Müller or proportional counter. When the Th^{234} has eluted, switch to an eluting solution of 9 M HCl–1 M HF and continue as before. After elution of the Pa^{234} activity (count on a Geiger-Müller counter), again change the eluting solution, this time to 0.1 M HCl and remove the U^{238} (counting for alphas with a proportional counter).

Data:

Plot the cpm versus the plate number, indicating on the graph the eluting solution used in each range. Look up Kraus, Moore, and Nelson, *J. Am. Chem. Soc.*, **78**, 2692 (1956), and Kraus and Nelson, First Geneva Conference, Vol. 7, 113-136 (1955), to discuss the chemistry involved in this experiment. *N.B.* Save the Th^{234} fraction for Experiment 28.

Solvent Extraction

In solvent extraction, the desired metal ion is distributed between two immiscible liquid phases, one of which is usually an aqueous solution, the other an organic solvent. In order to possess sufficient solubility in the organic phase, the metal ion must be in the form of a neutral desolvated species. This means that an uncharged complex utilizing all the coordination sites of the metal ion must exist prior to extraction. This neutral species distributes itself between the two liquid phases according to the Berthelot-Nernst homogeneous distribution law which has been discussed in the section on coprecipitation.

For the distribution of metal ion A^{+n} in the neutral complex form AX, the equilibrium is

$$AX(C_1) \rightleftharpoons AX(C_2) \tag{IX-11}$$

where C_1 and C_2 are the concentrations of AX in the aqueous and organic phases, respectively. The thermodynamic expression for the distribution is

$$K = \frac{a_2}{a_1} = \frac{\gamma_2 C_2}{\gamma_1 C_1} = \frac{\gamma_2}{\gamma_1} K_D \tag{IX-12}$$

K is a valid thermodynamic constant dependent on temperature but not on concentration. Since it is quite unlikely that the ratio of the activity coefficients, γ_2/γ_1, remains a constant for two dissimilar phases as the concentration changes, K_D is not independent of concentration except over a limited range. Experimentally it may be difficult to ascertain the concen-

tration of AX if the metal ion is not all in this form in both phases. In the aqueous phase uncomplexed or lesser complexed species may be present while in the organic phase polymerization or dissociation of the complex may occur after extraction. To avoid the necessity of determining these effects, a distribution ratio for the metal ion is defined for any set of experimental conditions.

$$D = \frac{\text{total concentration in organic phase}}{\text{total concentration in aqueous phase}} \qquad \text{(IX-13)}$$

The effectiveness of a particular system in separating two ions, A and B is expressed by the ratio of their distribution ratios.

$$\beta = \frac{D_A}{D_B} \qquad \text{(IX-14)}$$

To express the completeness of an extraction the per cent extraction, $\%E$, is used:

$$\%E = \frac{100D}{D + (V_W/V_O)} \qquad \text{(IX-15a)}$$

where V_W and V_O are the volumes of the aqueous and the organic phases. If V_W and V_O are equal, this reduces to

$$\%E = \frac{100D}{D + 1} \qquad \text{(IX-15b)}$$

Because neutral species only are extractable, the nature of the complex formed by the metal ion is of interest. Two general types of complexes are of use: (1) chelate systems and (2) ion-association systems.

Chelate Systems

Complexes with a high degree of covalent character are formed by the interaction of metal ions with polydentate organic ions. These chelates are very stable and the organic groups usually occupy all the coordination sites of the central metal ion. Since the net effect is to form a covalent molecule with an external organic framework surrounding the metal atom, it is not surprising that many of these chelates exhibit appreciable solubility in organic solvents.

Acetylacetone, 8-hydroxy quinoline, dimethylglyoxime, cupferron, dithizone, and thenoyltrifluoroacetone are a few of the chelating agents used in extraction systems. Thenoyltrifluoroacetone (TTA) has been used particularly with the lanthanide and actinide elements but, as may be seen in Figure 5, it is capable of providing excellent separations between many other elements. The effect of pH at constant reagent concentration on these chelate extractions is also evident in this figure.

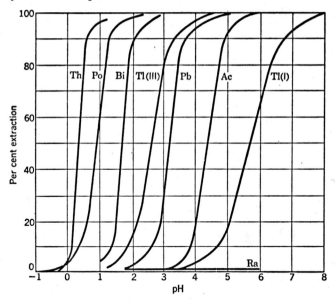

Figure 5. Effect of pH on the extraction of some heavy elements from aqueous solution by an equal volume of 0.25 M TTA in benzene. [F. T. Hagemann, *J. Am. Chem. Soc.*, **72**, 768 (1950)]

Ion-association Systems

There are three general types of coordination compounds important in extraction which do not involve chelation. In all cases the coordination of organic species imparts sufficient organic nature to an ion pair to provide solubility in the organic phase. The metal ion may be coordinated by large organic groups to form either cationic or anionic species which form ion pairs with large counter ions. Ketones, ethers and many other oxygen containing organic solvents may act as Lewis bases and through coordi-

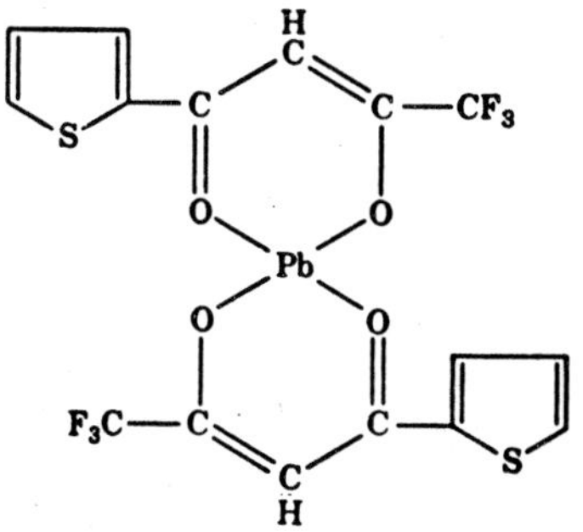

Figure 6. Lead thenoyltrifluoracetonate.

nation occupy in association with inorganic anions all the coordination
sites of the metal ion. Finally, some high molecular weight organic anions
form salts which act much as soaps do to form aggregates called micelles
in the solvents.

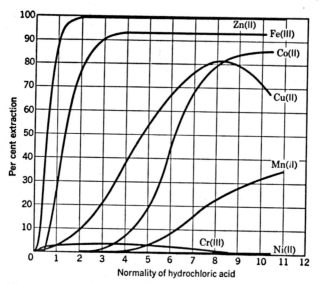

Figure 7. The effect of acid concentration on extraction from
aqueous HCl solutions by an equal volume of an 8% solution
of methyl dioctylamine in trichloroethylene. [Mahlman,
Leddicotte, and Moore, *Anal. Chem.*, **26**, 12 (1954)]

A number of tertiary amines which have this property have been shown
to be usable in extraction systems. Since, in contact with an aqueous solution, the cations may be exchanged for others present in the aqueous
phase, these amine systems show marked similarity to anion resin exchange.

TABLE I

Extraction from 6M Hydrochloric Acid
with an Equal Volume of Ethyl Ether

Metal Ion	% Extracted	Metal Ion	% Extracted
As(III)	68	Mo(VI)	80–90
As(V)	2–4	Te(IV)	34
Au(III)	95	Tl(III)	90–95
Fe(III)	99	Sb(III)	6
Ga(III)	97	Sb(V)	81
Ge(IV)	40–60	Sn(II)	15–30
Hg(II)	0.2	Sn(IV)	17
Ir(IV)	5	Zn(II)	0.2

Very low or no extraction: Ag, Al, Be, Bi, Ca, Cd, Cr, Co, Cu, Fe (II), In, Mn, Ni,
Os, Pb, Pd (II), Pt (IV), Rh, Se, Th, Ti, U, V, W, Zr, lanthanides.

Following extraction, these ion-association complexes interact in the organic phase much more than the chelate complexes. Polymerization at higher and dissociation at lower concentrations introduce considerable uncertainty in the actual extracting form. Tables I and II give data on two

TABLE II

Extraction from 8M Nitric Acid with an Equal Volume of Ethyl Ether

Metal Ion	% Extracted	Metal Ion	% Extracted
As(V)	14	Np(VI)	82
Bi(III)	7	P(V) as $(NH_4)_2HPO_4$	20
Ce(IV)	97	Th(IV)	35
Cr(VI)	>15	Tl(III)	8
Au(III)	97	U(VI)	65
Hg(II)	5	Zr(IV)	8

of the most valuable systems of this type. High electrolyte concentration in the aqueous phase can increase extraction into the organic phase by lowering the dielectric constant and reducing the activity of the water. If the electrolyte has an anion which coordinates with the metal ion, the electrolyte salting out reagent also increases extraction through the mass action effect.

Kinetics of Solvent Extraction

The rate of complex formation in the aqueous phase and the rate of transfer of the complex across the liquid-liquid interface determine the kinetics of solvent extraction. The first process may be measurably slow in many chelate systems. However, since the aqueous phase is usually prepared a little while before extraction, the rate of chelation is not a major factor in most practical separations. The rate of transfer is relatively fast, allowing equilibrium to be established in a rather short time when the two phases are agitated. The velocity of the two phases relative to each other (as well as the area of interface) determines the rate of transfer and this is not necessarily increased by very rapid agitation which may cause increased motion of both phases without changing greatly their relative velocities. Consequently, continuous inversion or shaking at a normal rate for several minutes is sufficient to obtain partition equilibrium in most systems.

Experimental

The use of solvent extraction in separation schemes offers several advantages to the radiochemist. It is frequently quite selective and can be used to extract the desired element or to remove contaminants. Extraction

can be used prior to a precipitation to remove impurities which might coprecipitate. If the distribution ratios are large, extraction with several successive volumes or a continuous counter current procedure allows removal of all but negligible amounts of the solute in relatively short times.

In batch extraction the two liquid phases are shaken until equilibrium is reached, then after settling, are separated. The equation for the weight of solute (W_n) remaining in an aqueous solution of volume v_2 after extraction by n successive portions of organic phase is

$$W_n = W\left[\frac{v_1}{Dv_2 + v_1}\right]^n \qquad \text{(IX-16)}$$

where W is the original weight of solute in the aqueous phase, D the distribution ratio and v_2 the volume of the organic phase in each of the n portions. It can be calculated easily from this equation that extraction by several smaller portions of the organic phase is more efficient than by one large portion.

After extraction, the solute is frequently back extracted into a fresh aqueous phase. For example, following extraction of thorium into a 0.25 M TTA-benzene solution from a solution of $pH = 1$ (Figure 5), back extraction into an aqueous phase of $pH = 0$ provides very good selectivity for thorium.

Examples of the use of solvent extraction were seen in the two organic Szilard-Chalmers experiments, Nos. 18 and 19. In Chapter X, a TTA extraction is used to ascertain the oxidation number of promethium (Experiment 33). In Chapter XI labeled benzoic acid is used to study the efficiency of extraction of that acid by ether (Experiment 38).

If a recorder and count rate meter are not available for Experiment 28, a Geiger-Müller counter may be used with one person keeping track of the time and recording the total registered counts as the other partner reads them out every 15 seconds without interruption in the count itself (see the description of Experiment 17). If a well-scintillation counter is available, after centrifugation the organic layer may be transferred to a test tube and counted for gammas as a liquid sample.

EXPERIMENT 28

Solvent Extraction

Purpose:

To use solvent extraction to study Pa^{234m} after rapid separation from Th^{234}.

Method:

See the instructions in Experiment 17 for preparing the rate meter and recorder. In this experiment the Pa^{234m} of slightly over one minute half life will be studied.

Dissolve the Th^{234} from Experiment 27 in 1 ml of 8 N HCl and allow it to stand at least overnight. Prepare 10 ml of a 5% solution of tri-iso-octyl amine in xylene and contact this intimately with an equal volume of 8 N HCl by stirring or shaking.

(1) Add 1 ml of the organic solution to the Th solution. From here on speed is essential. Stir vigorously for 20 seconds, centrifuge for 20 seconds then transfer the organic layer to a stainless steel cupped disc and evaporate under a heat lamp. Then count as in Experiment 17. After the first 5 minutes, stop the recorder count and take a count on a Geiger-Müller counter. Take a count the next morning and again that afternoon.

(2) After the initial 5 minute count of the sample from step 1, add another ml of the organic solution to the Th solution and repeat the extraction and counting.

Data:

Determine the half life of the Pa^{234m}. Which were the best data, (1) or (2)? Discuss the reason for this. *N.B.* It would be well to plan every step very carefully in this experiment and first practice the extraction and evaporation without the Th.

Paper Chromatography

A strip of filter paper will absorb water vapor up to 20% of its own weight. If it is placed in contact with an organic phase, the paper serves as a support for a stationary aqueous phase in partition chromatography. This aqueous phase may be considered as a concentrated solution of carbohydrate just as the resin phase of an ion exchanger, or may be considered a concentrated polyelectrolyte solution phase. Solutes will be distributed between this aqueous phase and the organic phase in different ratios depending on their relative sorbability in the two phases. The basis of this sorption is quite complex, in some cases being solubility partition between two immiscible solvents, in others being true adsorption on the cellulose fibers. In still other experiments, ion exchange with the free carboxyl groups of the cellulose network has been shown to occur when mineral acid-organic solvent mixtures are used as the mobile phase. The behavior is then similar to that of a weak base ion exchanger.

Paper chromatography in operation is rather simple. The solutes to be separated are placed near one end of a strip of filter paper either as a small round spot or as a thin strip. This end is dipped in the developing solvent

below this spot and by capillary action the solvent is drawn up the paper. After sufficient development, the chromatogram is removed and dried. The separated spots or zones are detected in some suitable fashion. These separated components may then be recovered by leaching or by ashing of the paper. The amount of movement of a solute in most systems is not dependent on the composition of the mixture of solutes and is the same for macro and micro quantities. For this reason and because of its simplicity, paper chromatography is a very important analytical technique to the organic and biochemist working with labeled mixtures on a micro scale. For mixtures of simple inorganic ions, the ion exchange and solvent extraction techniques are usually more important, chiefly due to the greater rapidity of separation possible.

The amount of separation which can be achieved in a system is calculated from comparison of the R_f value of each component of the mixture for that system. The definition of R_f is

$$R_f = \frac{\text{distance traveled by the solute}}{\text{distance traveled by the solvent front}}$$

The R_f value of a solute is specific to each system and is directly related to the partition function of the solute in the system. The latter is in turn dependent on the nature of the solvent and the temperature. Conditions must be carefully controlled if R_f values are to be reproducible. It is very important that the vapor in the chromatographic chamber be saturated with the solvent vapor. The solvents themselves must be presaturated with water and often a small dish of water must be placed in the chamber during development to prevent evaporation of water from the paper. Ascending development is used in Experiments 29 and 30, but descending movement is used commonly also, although the apparatus is a little more complicated in that case.

After development, solutions of reagents are applied to the chromatogram to detect inactive solutes. This is done either by painting or by spraying although it is often difficult to obtain uniform spraying over the total area. Gases may be passed over the paper (e.g., H_2S). In all cases, a colored complex is formed. The task of detection, especially for quantitative measurements, is greatly simplified if the solutes are radioactive. The chromatogram may be cut in small sections and each counted individually. Alternately, the uncut chromatogram may be scanned along its length with a counter or an autoradiogram may be prepared with film. If the solutes are inactive, after development the chromatogram may be reacted with a radioactive reagent which will form insoluble derivatives with the solutes. The excess, unreacted reagent is washed away before the chromatogram is counted.

In the detection of the spots in the chromatogram of a mixture of amino acids, active reagents have been used in several ways. The N-*p*-I-phenyl sulfonyl derivatives of the amino acids are prepared and chromatographed. Either the iodine or the sulfur may be labeled in this reagent.[3] Another method exposes the developed amino acid chromatogram to labeled methyl iodide.[4] In analogous fashion, detection of fatty acid spots on a developed chromatogram may be accomplished by forming the fatty acid salts of radioactive cobalt.[5] Members of a related family will yield active spots so identification of the individual members depends on knowledge of the R_f values or subsequent analysis.

Experimental

No specific experiments are included in this text which involve autoradiography. However, these two experiments with paper chromatographic techniques are easily adapted to the inclusion of autoradiography. After development by drying of the chromatogram (before application of $AgNO_3$ or Na_2S), they may be placed in close contact with a piece of medical X-ray film and left in the dark for several days. Development in Kodak D-19 and intensification with Kodak Chromium Intensifier In-4 yields dark spots at the sites of the radioactive species along the chromatogram. The R_f values obtained by autoradiography may be compared with those obtained by counting and spraying with a chemical reagent.

EXPERIMENT 29

Paper Chromatography (I)[6]

Purpose:

To separate Na^{22} tracer from Mg in solution.

Method:

Prepare a $MgCl_2$ or $Mg(NO_3)_2$ solution of such a concentration that 50 microliters will contain 2–3 micrograms of Mg. Also prepare a solution of ethanol containing 20% water. In a 100 ml graduated cylinder, add enough alcohol to reach the 10 ml mark. Cut a strip of Whatman No. 1 Chromatography Paper (0.5 in. wide) long enough to reach from the end of a copper wire hook in a cork for the top of the graduated cylinder to about 0.5 cm below the solution level.

[3] E. Lederer, and M. Lederer, *Chromatography*, 2nd ed. New York: D. Van Nostrand Co., Inc., 1957.

[4] F. P. W. Winteringham, A. Harrison, R. G. Bridges, *Analyst*, 77, 19 (1952).

[5] H. P. Kaufmann, J. Budwig, *Fette U. Seifen*, 53, 69, 253, 390, 408 (1951).

[6] Lederer, *Anal. Chem. Acta.*, 8, 134 (1953).

Add 50 microliters of the Mg solution and approximately 5000 cpm of Na^{22} tracer to several drops of 6 M HCl on a glass counting disc. Evaporate to dryness under an infrared heat lamp. Add 10 microliters of 6 M HCl to the disc. After moving this volume around on the disc with the tip of the micropipet to dissolve all the Mg and Na^{22}, transfer it to the paper, spreading it along a previously marked thin line. This line should be marked so that the solution level in the cylinder will be at least 1.5–2 cm below it. Dry gently under a heat lamp; then, suspend the strip from the copper hook and introduce it into the cylinder, noting the time.

Allow the chromatogram to develop for approximately 5 hours. After this time, remove the paper strip and carefully dry it. Use a perfume atomizer to spray the dry strip gently with a solution of 0.1 N silver nitrate. Alternately, the $AgNO_3$ solution may be carefully daubed onto the paper strip, using a piece of absorbent tissue (wear gloves). Exposure to sunlight will yield a darkened area indicating the location of the $MgCl_2$.

Cut and number the paper in 1 cm lengths and count each in a sodium iodide scintillation counter or a Geiger-Müller counter.

Data:

Plot a profile of the chromatogram in terms of Na^{22} activity versus distance from origin; also, one for the relative darkening (estimated). How could the Na^{22} be recovered? Estimate the amount of Mg which would still be in the Na^{22} (be willing to lose some of the Na^{22} if this would decrease the Mg contamination a fair amount). Calculate R_f values for Na and Mg in this particular system.

EXPERIMENT 30

Paper Chromatography (II)[7]

Purpose:

To separate Bi^{210} and Po^{210} from the parent Pb^{210}.

Method:

(1) Prepare a saturated solution of $Pb(NO_3)_2$ acidified to a pH of 2.5 with nitric acid. Pipet onto a counting planchet a small amount of the Pb^{210} tracer solution. The tracer solution should be old enough so that the Bi^{210} and Po^{210} daughters are in equilibrium with the Pb^{210}. Count the assay with a thin window Geiger-Müller or a proportional counter, using an aluminum absorber of 10–15 mg per cm' to prevent counting of the soft

[7] F. W. Lima, *J. Chem. Ed.*, **31**, 153 (1954).

beta (0.02 Mev) emissions of Pb^{210} and the alpha emissions of Po^{210}. Based on this counting assay, add approximately 50,000 cpm of activity to 100 microliters of the $Pb(NO_3)_2$ solution.

In a 100 ml graduated cylinder, add enough butanol (saturated with 3 N HCl) to reach the 10 ml mark. Cut a strip of Whatman No. 1 Chromatography Paper (0.5 in. wide) long enough to reach from the end of a copper wire hook in a cork for the top of the graduated cylinder to approximately 0.5 cm below the solution level.

Slowly add 10 microliters of the active $Pb(NO_3)_2$ solution along a thin line on the paper strip so that this line will be approximately 2 cm above the solution level. Dry the added solution carefully, affix the paper strip to the copper hook and place it carefully in the cylinder. Note the time of introduction. Be careful that the paper strip is hanging free of the wall of the cylinder.

Allow the chromatogram to develop for 5 hours, then remove the paper strip from the cylinder and carefully dry it. An autoradiogram may be prepared at this point. The chromatogram is then cut into 0.5 cm lengths and counted with a thin window Geiger-Müller or proportional counter. Absorption techniques may be used to identify the three active spots by the types and relative energy of the radiations.

(2) The experiment may be repeated using 10 microliters of the inactive $Pb(NO_3)_2$ solution which has been made 0.1 N in $Bi(NO_3)_3$ also. After development and drying, the strip is sprayed with a solution of Na_2S.

Data:

Calculate the R_f values for Pb, Bi, and Po from the counting and autoradiographic data. If part (2) has been performed, calculate R_f values for Pb and Bi when present in macro quantities. Compare the R_f value for Bi^{210} (micro) with that for Bi in part (2) (macro). *N.B.* If the instructor desires, the isolated and purified Pb^{210}, Bi^{210} and Po^{210} fractions may be counted over a period of time to study the genetic relationships and half lives involved.

Volatilization

A very useful technique for preparing carrier-free samples is that of volatilization. I_2, At, $GeCl_4$, $AsCl_3$, $SeCl_4$, OsO_4, RuO_4, Re_2O_7, and Tc_2O_7 are some compounds which can be distilled easily. Mercury is distilled as the metal at relatively low temperatures. Many other elements may be volatilized in a vacuum as the metal or the oxide at higher temperatures. This technique constitutes a common method of target preparation for accelerator irradiations. During such irradiations and during dissolution of targets after irradiation, volatile activities may be lost unless care is taken.

REFERENCES

Precipitation

Ayres, G. H., *Quantitative Chemical Analysis*. New York: Harper & Bros., 1958.

Friedlander, G., and J. W. Kennedy, *Nuclear and Radiochemistry*. New York: John Wiley & Sons, Inc., 1955, Chapter 2.

Williams, R. R., *Principles of Nuclear Chemistry*. New York: D. Van Nostrand Co., Inc., 1950.

Electrodeposition

Dodson, et al., *Miscellaneous Physical and Chemical Techniques of the Los Alamos Project*. New York: McGraw-Hill Book Co., Inc., 1952, Chapter 1.

Slatis, H., *Beta- and Gamma-Ray Spectroscopy*. New York: Interscience Publishers, Inc., 1955, Chapter 8.

Ion Exchange

Kitchener, J. A., *Ion Exchange Resins*. New York: John Wiley & Sons, Inc., 1957.

Kraus, K. A., "Ion Exchange," *Trace Analysis*, Yoe and Kock (eds.). New York: John Wiley & Sons, Inc., 1957.

Kraus, K. A., and F. Nelson, *Ann. Rev. Nuclear Sci.*, **7**, 31 (1957).

Kraus, K. A., and F. Nelson, *Proceedings of the International Conference on the Peaceful Uses of Atomic Energy* (Geneva: United Nations), Vol. **7** (1956), Paper 837.

Kunin, R., *Ion Exchange Resins*, 2nd ed. New York: John Wiley & Sons, Inc., 1958.

Stewart, D. C., *Proceedings of the International Conference on the Peaceful Uses of Atomic Energy* (Geneva: United Nations), Vol. **7** (1956), Paper 729.

Samuelson, O., *Ion Exchangers in Analytical Chemistry*. New York: John Wiley & Sons, Inc., 1953.

Solvent Extraction

Irving, H. M., *Quart. Rev.*, **5**, 200 (1951).

Martin, F. S., and R. J. W. Holt, *Quart. Rev.*, **4**, 327 (1959).

Morrison, G. H., and H. Freiser, *Solvent Extraction in Analytical Chemistry*. New York: John Wiley & Sons, Inc., 1957.

Paper Chromatography

Frierson, N. J., and J. W. Jones, *Anal. Chem.*, **23**, 1447 (1951).

Lederer, E., and M. Lederer, *Chromatography*, 2nd ed. New York: D. Van Nostrand Co., Inc., 1957.

Yagoda, H., *Radioactive Measurements with Nuclear Emulsions*. New York: John Wiley & Sons, Inc., 1949.

Volatilization

Dodson, et al., *Miscellaneous Physical and Chemical Techniques of the Los Alamos Project.* New York: McGraw-Hill Book Co., Inc., 1952.

Frauenfelder, H., *Helv. Phys. Acta.*, **23,** 347 (1950).

Sherwin, C. W., *Rev. Sci. Instr.*, **22,** 339 (1951).

X

Uses of Radioactive Tracers

IN THIS chapter a few of the experimental uses of radioactive tracers are studied. In many systems the use of isotopic tracers is justified by convenience, since ordinary techniques are capable of giving the same answers. There are some studies, such as isotopic exchange and self-diffusion, that can be carried out only by using tracers. It is not absolutely necessary to use radioactive isotopes because the same information can be obtained with stable separated isotopes. However, radioactive isotopes are, in general, much cheaper than separated stable isotopes and the necessity of final measurement by mass spectrometry in the case of the latter makes their measurement more costly in time and instrumentation. In the case of the few elements such as He, Li, B, N, O for which no active tracer of suitable half life exists, the stable isotope technique must be employed.

The basic assumption underlying the use of tracer techniques is that all the isotopes of a given element possess chemical identity and no change in the isotopic ratios occurs in the chemical or physical process under investigation. The validity of this assumption is dependent upon the degree of precision with which these ratios are measured as a slight dependence on mass does exist. For the usual standards of precision, isotopic fractionation is insignificant except in the very lightest elements. Even for carbon, in the large majority of systems, no isotopic effect is seen between C^{12} and C^{14}. On the other hand, the use of deuterium and tritium as hydrogen tracers must be carefully assessed for isotopic effects as the percentage differences in mass are much greater.

The second assumption implicit in the tracer technique is that the radioactivity of the tracers does not affect the chemical system. Before their decay, the active atoms behave as normal isotopes of the element and the only difference possible is that mentioned in the previous paragraph. These active atoms are detectable only at the moment of disintegration after which they are no longer isotopic with the parent (except in the case of isomeric transition). Should the level of activity be fairly high, it is possible that radiation effects could influence the chemical behavior of the system. These effects are discussed more fully in Chapter XII.

If the daughter atoms are also radioactive, then it may be necessary to discriminate between the two activities. For example, since strontium and yttrium are not chemically identical, a gross beta count of a strontium sample may include an unknown fraction of the Y^{90} activity present from Sr^{90} decay. Beta absorption measurements or gamma scintillation techniques are frequently useful in these cases. If equilibrium is rapidly established between the two activities, it is frequently simpler to count the samples after sufficient time for this to occur. If Cs^{137} is being used to study cesium chemistry, it is only necessary to wait 15 to 20 minutes after a separation to count a sample as Ba^{137m} reaches an equilibrium level in that time. Since the ratio of Ba to Cs activities in all samples is the same at equilibrium, the total count rate before and after a chemical step is then a true measure of the behavior of cesium alone.

In many cases it is necessary or expedient to use an active nuclide which undergoes significant decay during the chemical investigation. In order to compare results at different points in the process, it is necessary to correct all counts to the same point in time.

Isotope Exchange Reactions

If two different chemical species with some atom in common are mixed in solution, exchange of this common component may occur. The chemical equation would have the form

$$AX + BX^* = AX^* + BX \qquad \text{(X-1)}$$

Since the chemical species will be unchanged, it is impossible to observe the exchange unless the atoms in one reactant are tagged. By using X^*, a radioactive isotope of X, the reaction may be followed, and it is perhaps obvious that at equilibrium the activity should be uniformly distributed between the two chemical species—i.e., the specific activity of X^* will be the same for both AX and BX. Of course, if AX and BX are both strong

electrolytes, then uniform distribution is essentially immediate upon mixing. If at least one of the reactants is an inorganic complex or an organic molecule, the exchange is often measurably slow, if it occurs at all. It is possible to use these exchange reactions to gain information on the mechanism of exchange, as well as on complex formation, dissociation, nonequivalence of atoms in a molecule, and lability of coordination compounds.

Since the chemical form of the reactants is not altered by the isotopic exchange, there is no change in heat content. However, the entropy of the total system is increased when uniformity is achieved throughout the system in the distribution of the isotopes of X. This entropy increase provides a decrease in the free energy, making isotopic exchange a spontaneous reaction. Despite this spontaneity, the exchange may be prevented or made very slow by a large energy of activation requirement in the formation of a necessary transition state.

Mechanism Studies

Three possible rate determining mechanisms have been suggested for exchange reactions. In the first, the reversible dissociation of one reactant is followed by exchange of one of the dissociation products with the second reactant. This seems to be a less common mode of exchange than the next two mechanisms. The second exchange path involves the transfer of electrons. If inactive Fe(III) is mixed with active Fe(II), the activity distributes uniformly between both valence states. Since it is unlikely that this electron exchange occurs by a direct interaction between the two positive ions which repel each other, it is postulated that the anion serves as a bridge. If this is the case, the reaction would be

$$Fe^*(II) + X^- + Fe(III) = Fe^* \cdot \cdot X^- \cdot \cdot Fe = Fe^*(III) + X^- + Fe(II)$$

The third path suggested is the transfer of atoms where a transition state decomposes with rearrangement of bonds. The exchange between molecular iodine and iodide ion proceeds via the stable intermediate triiodide ion.

$$I^- + I{-}I^* = (I{-}I{-}I^*)^- = I{-}I + I^{*-}$$

An unstable transition state is postulated in the exchange between a halide ion and an alkyl halide. This reaction proceeds via a Walden inversion.

The rate of the exchange is strongly dependent on the nature of R_1, R_2, and R_3. If these groups provide steric hindrance to the formation of the transition complex, the result is a relatively large activation energy. This accounts for the fact that at room temperature these are not ordinarily rapid exchanges. The nature of the solvent also has a marked effect on the rate which increases markedly in non-aqueous solvents. If the central carbon atom is asymmetric, the isotope exchange as expected from the mechanism results in inversion of optical activity.

For the exchange reaction represented in (X-1), the rate of increase of AX^* is equal to the rate of formation minus the rate of destruction of AX^*. The rate of formation is the product of the rate of reaction (R), the fraction of reactions which occur with an active BX^* and the fraction of reactions which occur with an inactive AX. Using the following notation

$$a = (AX) + (AX^*)$$
$$b = (BX) + (BX^*)$$
$$x = (AX^*)$$
$$y = (BX^*)$$

the rate of formation equals $R \cdot \dfrac{y}{b} \cdot \dfrac{(a - x)}{a}$. In similar fashion, the rate of destruction equals $R \cdot \dfrac{x}{a} \cdot \dfrac{b - y}{b}$. Therefore

$$\frac{dx}{dt} = R \cdot \frac{y}{b} \cdot \frac{(a - x)}{a} - R \cdot \frac{x}{a} \cdot \frac{(b - y)}{b}$$

$$\frac{dx}{dt} = \frac{R}{ab} (ay - bx) \tag{X-2}$$

The solution of this equation is

$$\ln (1 - F) = -\frac{a + b}{ab} Rt \tag{X-3}$$

where $F = x_t/x_\infty$ (x_∞ is the value of x_t at $t = \infty$, i.e., equilibrium). The rate of exchange R is evaluated from the slope of a plot of log $(1 - F)$ versus t. If more than one rate of exchange is present due to exchange with non-equivalent atoms in a reactant, it may be very difficult to resolve this curve sufficiently to obtain values for the reaction rates.

Structural Studies

The study of exchange rates can add to our knowledge of the bond character in complexes and molecules. It is to be expected that covalently bonded atoms would exchange more slowly than those ionically bonded. In complexes of the type MX_n, the rate of exchange of the central metal ion M is not necessarily a valid measure of the lability of the M—X bonds as exchange requires rupture of n number of M—X bonds. Exchange of the complexing ligand X, on the other hand, requires rupture of only one

M—X bond and, consequently, is a good indication of the character of the bond. If X is a polydentate chelating agent, then exchange again requires severance of several bonds and is slower. Several generalizations have been made concerning ligand exchange in metal complexes:[1]

(1) Transition metal complexes are more inert than analogous non-transition metal compounds;

(2) Metal ions of the d^3, d^6, and d^8 systems are among the more inert complexes; e.g. Ni(II) complexes exchange more slowly than the same Cu(II) complexes;

(3) The greater the polydentate character of the chelating agent, the slower the exchange;

(4) Complexes of higher coordination number are less liable to exchange than those of lower coordination number for the same complexing agent;

(5) The greater the charge on the central metal atom, the more inert the complex to exchange.

In molecules containing more than one of the exchanging atoms, it may be possible to obtain information on the equivalence of these atoms in the molecule. For example, for PCl_5 and Cl_2 it was found that in CCl_4 solution, 3 of the chlorine atoms of PCl_5 exchange immeasurably fast while the other two exchange relatively slowly.[2] PCl_5 has a trigonal bypyramid structure (Figure 1) which X-ray studies have shown to have the 2 apical chlorines at 2.11Å and the 3 equatorial chlorines at 2.04Å from the central phosphorous. Since these two types of chlorines are not equivalent, it is not unexpected that different exchange rates are observed.

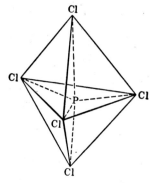

Figure 1. Structure of phosphorus pentachloride, a trigonal bipyramid with P in the equatorial plane.

It has been shown that the two sulfur atoms in thiosulfate ion are nonequivalent and do not exchange. If active sulfur is added to sodium sulfite solution, labeled thiosulfate is formed. Acidification of the solution decomposes the thiosulfate. If the SO_2 evolved from the solution is collected, it is found to contain no activity, indicating no exchange.[3] The reactions are

[1] F. Basolo and R. G. Pearson, *Mechanisms of Inorganic Reactions* (New York: John Wiley & Sons, Inc., 1958, 397).

[2] J. Downs and R. E. Johnson, *J. Am. Chem. Soc.*, **77**, 2098 (1955).

[3] W. J. McCool and R. R. Hentz, *J. Chem. Educ.*, **32**, 329 (1955).

$$S^* + \left[\begin{array}{cc} O & O \\ & S \\ & \| \\ & O \end{array}\right]^{2-} = \left[\begin{array}{cc} O & O \\ & S \\ S^* & O \end{array}\right]^{2-} \xrightarrow{H^+} S^* + SO_2 \uparrow + H_2O$$

Similar exchange studies have been used to show that nickel cyanide probably exists in the crystal structure as $Ni[Ni(CN)_4]$ rather than $Ni(CN)_2$ (see Experiment 32).

The use of tracers in reaction studies is not restricted to isotopic exchange only. In the common physicochemical techniques for kinetic studies, the forward and reverse reaction rates are measured when the reaction is well displaced from equilibrium, whereas the equilibrium constant is determined when the system is at equilibrium. If tracers are used, it is usually possible to measure the reaction rates as well as the equilibrium constant at equilibrium. It is also possible to observe the behavior of a particular atom of a reactant molecule through the course of a reaction. This can contribute greatly to understanding the mechanism of complicated reactions.

Experimental

The exchange between ethyl iodide and iodide ion proceeds via a bimolecular mechanism, as discussed previously. The reaction rate expression should be second order, i.e.

$$\frac{-d(I^*)}{dt} = k_2(RI)(I^*) \tag{X-4}$$

If the concentration of one reactant is made much larger than that of the second, the concentration of this reactant remains essentially unchanged during the course of the reaction. The rate equation becomes pseudo first order in this situation and if ethyl iodide is the reactant in excess, Equation (X-4) becomes

$$\frac{-d(I^*)}{dt} = k'(I^*)$$

where
$$k' = k_2(RI) \tag{X-5}$$

Upon integration, setting the initial time as $t = 0$, Equation X-6 is obtained

$$\ln (I^*)_t - \ln (I^*)_0 = -k't \tag{X-6}$$

A plot of $\log (I^*)$ versus t should be linear with a slope equal to $-k'/2.303$. The pseudo first order reaction rate constant obtained may be used to calculate the second order reaction rate constant by dividing k' by the concentration of ethyl iodide.

The reactions of Experiment 32 may be represented by

(1) $Ni^{*2+} + Ni(CN)_4^{2-} = Ni^*[Ni(CN)_4] \rightleftharpoons Ni^*[Ni^*(CN)_4]$

(2) $Ni^*[Ni^*(CN)_4] + DMG = Ni^*DMG + [Ni^*(CN)_4]^{2-}$

Ni^{63} emits a low energy beta ray ($E_{max} = 67$ kev). Therefore, if the comparisons are to be valid, care must be taken while counting to see that the samples are relatively thin and in the same chemical state.

EXPERIMENT 31

Isotopic Exchange Reaction[4]

Purpose:

To use tracers to study the kinetics of an isotopic exchange reaction for an organic compound.

Method:

Prepare 6 ml of a 0.1 N sodium iodide solution in ethanol, containing about 10,000–20,000 cpm of I^{131}. Also prepare a solution of 0.9 M ethyl iodide in ethanol. Place these solutions in a bath whose temperature can be maintained between 40–45° reasonably well ($\pm 1°C$). Mix thoroughly by stirring exactly 5 ml of each in a 15 ml test tube, recording the time of addition. Keep the reaction mixture at the same temperature during the course of the experiment. Each 5 minutes, withdraw a 500 μl aliquot of the reaction mixture and stir it thoroughly into a mixture of 1 ml of H_2O and 1 ml of chloroform which had been prepared previously in a 15 ml centrifuge cone. Centrifuge this mixture until the 2 layers separate and remove the top layer with a transfer pipet into a cupped counting disc. Evaporate to dryness under a heat lamp and count in the Geiger-Müller or proportional counter. Take twelve samples at 5 minute intervals. As a thirteenth sample, pipet 250 μl of the original NaI solution into a counting disc and dry and count in the same fashion. This sample represents time zero.

Data:

Make a plot of the log of the count rate versus time of sample removal (using time of initial mixture as $t = 0$). Calculate from this plot:
  (1) the pseudo first order rate constant,
  (2) the second order rate constant,
  (3) the half life of the reaction.
What would be the effect of using 20°C rather than 40°C?

[4] H. A. C. McKay, *J. Am. Chem. Soc.*, **65**, 702 (1943).

EXPERIMENT 32

Structure of Nickel Cyanide[5]

Purpose:

To use an isotope exchange reaction to investigate the structure of nickel cyanide.

Method:

Approximately 2 grams of $K_2Ni(CN)_4$ should be obtained from the instructor. (It may also be synthesized easily—see the reference below). The sample is placed in a 50 ml beaker and dissolved in 15 ml of dilute hydrochloric acid. An aliquot of Ni^{63} tracer stock solution sufficient to provide between 5000 and 10,000 cpm is transferred to a second beaker and evaporated to dryness under a heat lamp. The aliquot of tracer solution also should contain 0.1–1 mg of inactive nickel. The residue is redissolved in 10 ml of dilute hydrochloric acid. Maintain the acidity of both solutions at a pH of 2. Pour both solutions together into a larger beaker and allow the mixture to stand for 5 minutes during which time a fine suspension of nickel cyanide will appear in the solution. Then add 50 ml of a 1% ethanolic solution of dimethylglyoxime (DMG) and allow the mixture to stand overnight. The precipitate is filtered through a filter assembly, the precipitate cake on the filter paper dried and counted in a proportional counter (or a Geiger-Müller counter if necessary). Add a large excess of DMG solution to the filtrate to ensure the complete precipitation of all the available nickel ion. Filter and count the second precipitate as before.

Determine the self-absorption factor of the nickel—DMG complex in the following manner. Dissolve the first precipitate in 5 M nitric acid, transfer the solution to a steel cup planchet and, after drying under a heat lamp, ignite the sample over a Fisher burner. Count the sample and calculate the self-absorption factor from the following expression:

$$f = \frac{\text{cpm of } Ni^{63} \text{ as oxide}}{\text{cpm of } Ni^{63} \text{ as DMG complex}}$$

To a steel planchet add a duplicate of the original aliquot of Ni^{63} stock solution, dry and ignite, then count.

[5] F. A. Long, *J. Am. Chem. Soc.*, **73**, 537 (1951). For the preparation of $K_2Ni(CN)_4$ see W. C. Fernelius and J. J. Burbage, *Inorganic Syntheses*, Vol. II (McGraw-Hill Book Co., Inc., 1946).

Data:

Calculate the per cent exchange in 5 minutes between $Ni^{(63)2+}$ and $Ni(CN)_4^{2-}$ from the original amount of Ni^{63} added and the total Ni^{63} in both DMG precipitates (based on the cpm as oxide). Discuss the meaning of this amount of exchange in this system based on the discussion in the text of "Structural Studies."

Determination of Ionic Charge

In Chapter IX the process of solvent extraction was discussed. In this experiment solvent extraction is used to measure the charge of a metal ion in tracer concentration. The β-diketone thenoyltrifluoroacetone is used to chelate promethium so that it may be extracted partially into benzene. The following equilibria are set up

$$HA \rightleftharpoons H^+ + A^- \qquad \begin{cases} HA = \text{the diketone} \\ M^{+z} = \text{the cation} \end{cases} \qquad (X\text{-}7)$$

$$M^{+z} + xA^- \rightleftharpoons MA_z \qquad\qquad\qquad\qquad\qquad (X\text{-}8)$$

The equilibrium constants are

$$K_A = \frac{[H^+][A^-]}{[HA]} \qquad (X\text{-}9)$$

and

$$K_{MA_z} = \frac{[MA_z]}{[M^{+z}][A^-]^z} \text{ (in the aqueous phase)} \qquad (X\text{-}10)$$

Also, from Equation (IX-12), the distribution constant is

$$K_D = \frac{[MA_z]_{aqueous}}{[MA_z]_{benzene}} \qquad (X\text{-}11)$$

Since only the species MA_z is extracted to any significant extent into the benzene, the distribution ratio (see Equation IX-13) is expressed by

$$D = \frac{\Sigma \text{ M in aqueous phase}}{\Sigma \text{ M in benzene phase}} = \frac{[MA_z]_{aqueous} + [M^{+z}]_{aqueous}}{[MA_z]_{benzene}}$$

$$D = K_D + \frac{[M^{+z}]_{aqueous}}{[MA_z]_{benzene}} \qquad (X\text{-}12)$$

From Equations (X-9) and (X-10), it can be shown that

$$[M^{+z}]_{aqueous} = \frac{[H^+]^z[MA_z]_{aqueous}}{K_{MA_z} \cdot K_A^z[HA]^z} = \frac{[H^+]^z[MA_z]_{aqueous}}{K_1[HA]^z} \qquad (X\text{-}13)$$

where $K_1 = K_{MA_z} \cdot K_A^z$. Therefore, substitution of (X-13) in (X-12) gives

$$D = K_D + \frac{[H^+]^z[MA_z]_{aqueous}}{K_1[HA]^z[MA_z]_{benzene}}$$

$$D = K_D + \frac{[H^+]^z}{K_1[HA]^z} \cdot K_D$$

If the pH is kept constant, this becomes

$$D = K_D + \frac{K_2}{[\mathrm{HA}]^x}$$ (X-14)

where

$$K_2 = \frac{K_D[\mathrm{H}^+]^x}{K_1}$$

By using a range of concentration of [HA] such that $D \gg K_D$, Equation (X-14) reduces to

$$D = \frac{K_2}{[\mathrm{HA}]^x}$$ (X-15)

$$\therefore \quad \log D = \log K_2 - x \log [\mathrm{HA}]$$

Therefore, a graph of $\log D$ versus $\log [\mathrm{HA}]$ should give a straight line whose slope will have a value of $-x$, where x is the charge of the metal ion. Promethium, the metal ion used in this experiment, is not found in nature, because it has no stable nor very long-lived isotopes. Consequently, studies of its chemistry must be done with radioactive isotopes and usually at tracer concentrations.

Anion resin exchange in an analogous manner has been used by Kraus and Nelson[6] to determine the charge of complex metal anions such as those formed by the alkaline earths with citrate ions. Cationic complexes have been studied using cation resin exchange by Connick.[7]

EXPERIMENT 33

Determination of Ionic Charge

Purpose:

To use solvent extraction to measure the ionic charge of promethium.

Method:

Prepare a stock solution of 0.20 M T.T.A. (thenoyltrifluoroacetone) in benzene and a buffer solution of pH 4.0. Dilute with benzene 1 ml of the stock 0.2 M T.T.A. solution as necessary to prepare 0.025, 0.05, 0.10, 0.15, and 0.20 M solutions. To 1 ml of the buffer solution, add a sufficient volume of tracer solution (preferably 5–10 microliters) to yield approximately 50,000 cpm of the Pm^{147} (as determined in a proportional or Geiger-Müller counter). Then, add 1 ml of the T.T.A. solution. Stir vigorously for

[6] K. Kraus and F. Nelson, *J. Am. Chem. Soc.*, 77, 801 (1955).

[7] R. E. Connick, Paper A-1064, Abstracts, XVIIth International Congress of Pure and Applied Chemistry, Munich (1959).

5 minutes, mixing the two phases intimately, then centrifuge the mixture for one minute to separate the two phases. Repeat this procedure with each T.T.A. concentration.

Withdraw duplicate 100 microliter aliquots from each phase of each sample and pipet into a 1 inch watch glass for evaporation under a heat lamp. Be certain to clean the pipet well between samples. After drying, count the samples taking care to reproduce the geometry as well as possible if a Geiger-Müller counter is used.

Data:

Calculate D for each concentration and plot log D as a function of the log of the T.T.A. concentration. Use a least squares analysis to obtain an experimental value for the charge of the Pm ion. Explain what approximations were made which may lead to experimental values slightly different than $+3.0$. Finally, draw the structural formula for the extracted complex.

Solubility Studies

The ease with which very low concentrations of radioactive solutes are determined makes tracer techniques a valuable tool in studies of slightly soluble substances. The change in solubility as a function of temperature can be measured by withdrawing a measured aliquot of the solution after establishment of equilibrium between solid and solution at various temperatures. This is facilitated if the aliquot may be counted directly in a gamma scintillation well counter.

For sparingly soluble electrolytes, at each temperature, an equilibrium constant may be expressed for the equilibrium between the crystal and the solution phase. If the reaction is

$$M_aX_b = aM^{b+} + bx^{a-}$$

the solubility product is given by

$$K_{sp} = a_+^a \cdot a_-^b \qquad \text{(X-16)}$$

where a_+ and a_- are the activities of the cation and anion, respectively. If m is the concentration and γ the activity coefficient of the ions, Equation (X-16) becomes

$$K_{sp} = (\gamma_+ m_+)^a (\gamma_- m_-)^b = m_+^a \cdot m_-^b (\gamma_\pm)^{a+b} \qquad \text{(X-17)}$$

The $\gamma_\pm$ is the mean activity coefficient of the ions, replacing the individual ionic activities. This mean activity coefficient has been shown experimentally to be approximately the same for a given strong electrolyte in all solutions of the same ionic equivalence. Lewis and Randall introduced the concept of ionic strength to express this ionic equivalence. The ionic strength of a solution of electrolytes is defined as

$$\mu = \tfrac{1}{2} \Sigma \, C_i Z_i^2 \qquad \text{(X-18)}$$

where C_i and Z_i are the molarity and valence of each ion in the solution. The ionic strength of a solution which is 0.1 N in KCl and 0.1 N in $Ba(NO_3)_2$ is

$$\mu = \tfrac{1}{2}[(0.1)(1)^2 + (0.1)(1)^2 + (0.1)(2)^2 + (0.2)(1)^2]$$
$$= \tfrac{1}{2}[0.1 + 0.1 + 0.4 + 0.2] = \tfrac{1}{2}[0.8]$$
$$\mu = 0.4$$

If the ionic strength of a dilute solution is known, the Debye-Huckel equation may be used to calculate the mean activity coefficient. This equation for dilute aqueous solutions at 25°C reduces to

$$\log \gamma_\pm = 0.509 Z_1 \cdot Z_2 \sqrt{\mu} \qquad \text{(X-19)}$$

where Z_1 and Z_2 are the ionic valences.

The fact that the presence of an added salt with no ion in common with a slightly soluble electrolyte increases the solubility of the latter may be explained by these equations. The presence of the added salt increases the total ionic strength of the solution which in turn causes a decrease in the mean activity coefficient of the slightly soluble electrolyte. In order that the constancy of the solubility product be maintained, the decrease in $\gamma_\pm$ must be offset by an increase in the solubility of the salt. This also allows determination of a very accurate value of K_{sp}. If the solubility is measured at a number of different ionic strengths, a K'_{sp} may be calculated at each ionic strength by using Equations (X-17) and (X-19). Extrapolation of a plot of K'_{sp} versus μ to $\mu = 0$ (where $\gamma_\pm = 1$) gives the true value of K_{sp}.

EXPERIMENT 34

Determination of K_{sp} of PbI_2

Purpose:

To use a tracer to determine the K_{sp} of PbI_2 and to check the validity of the Debye-Huckel equation.

Method:

Place 1.00 ml of a solution of NaI whose concentration is 6.5 mg NaI per ml in each of seven 50 ml beakers and add exactly the same amount of I^{131} to each (approximately 5×10^4 cpm). Set one beaker aside and treat each of the other six in the following fashion. Add 3 ml of $Pb(NO_3)_2$ solution (of 100 mg per ml concentration), stir and coagulate the precipitate. After cooling, filter (using a filter assembly) and wash the precipitate (with cold water). Then transfer each precipitate back to the 50 ml beaker. To the

first five beakers add 1.0 ml of a KNO_3 solution (0.05, 0.10, 0.25, 0.50, and 1.00 M in that order) and 1.0 ml of distilled water to the last. Slurry the precipitate in these six beakers for at least 20 minutes, then filter each, carefully collecting the filtrate and washings as quantitatively as possible. Since the solubility product of PbI_2 has a significant temperature coefficient, the closer the temperature is maintained constant between the solutions, the better will be the data. Record the temperature. To the six filtrates add 1.00 ml of the 6.5 mg per ml NaI solution. Then to these six solutions plus the original seventh beaker (set aside at the beginning of the experiment) add 3 ml of 25 mg per ml $AgNO_3$ solution. Coagulate the precipitate and filter. Mount and count the samples for I^{131}.

Data:

Calculate the solubility of PbI_2 for each sample and plot this versus the ionic strength of the solution. Use Equations (X-17) and (X-19) to calculate a value of K'_{sp} for each sample and plot log K'_{sp} as a function of $\mu^{1/2}$. Evaluate K_{sp} by extrapolation to $\mu = 0$ and compare with the literature value. Use this constant to calculate an experimental value of $\gamma_{\pm}$ (from Equation X-17) for each ionic strength and on the same graph plot these $\gamma_{\pm}$'s and those calculated by Equation (X-19) as a function of μ. Discuss this plot in terms of the validity of the Debye-Huckel expression.

Analytical Radiochemistry

Radioactivity may be used in many ways in chemical analysis. Neutron activation analysis (see Chapter VIII) is capable of extreme sensitivity, and as more high flux nuclear reactors are built, this should become a widely used technique. Quite a different aspect of activity, beta-ray backscattering, has been shown to hold promise as a useful analytical method.[8] However, the most common usage of radioactivity in analytical chemistry is in the application of tracer techniques. In some cases conventional analytical procedures have been modified to use tracers. In other cases new procedures have been established. Despite the large number of practical applications which have been demonstrated at the present time, it would seem that analytical chemists have only begun to exploit the potentialities of this new tool.

Radioactive tracers may be used to great advantage in the evaluation of a new or modified analytical procedure since they allow easy, accurate determination of the chemical yield of any step in the process. Tracers for both the desired component and for undesirable contaminants may be added and the fate of each species followed through each operation. The ability to detect very small amounts of activity make this a sensitive check on the degree of contamination. Precipitation, coprecipitation, extraction,

[8] P. R. Gray, D. H. Clarey, and W. H. Beamer, *Anal. Chem.*, **31**, 2065 (1959).

chromatography, electrodeposition, and distillation are a few of the analytical procedures which can be studied with tracers, as a review of the experiments of the last chapter will make evident. Usually the random error due to the counting measurement is on the order of 0.5–1%. In order that the over-all error be less than this, the phase containing the least amount of the tracer may be counted. For example, in a precipitation which is 99.5% complete, the over-all error is on the order of 0.5%, if the active precipitate is counted—too large for evaluation of the precipitation in most gravimetric analyses. However, the uncertainty is reduced to $5 \times 10^{-3}\%$ if the filtrate is counted with a 1% error, since the filtrate contains only 0.5% of the total activity. In this way the counting errors are minimized.

In many cases losses occur in the spray from evaporations of solutions. In ashing, volatilization or air currents may cause losses. These and many similar operations are conveniently checked quite sensitively with tracers.

Isotope Dilution

If knowledge of the percentage of some component of a rather complex mixture is desired, analysis may be accomplished by use of the technique of isotope dilution. To the mixture is added a small pure sample of the same compound as that under analysis. This addition is radioactive and its specific activity (cpm per gram) is very accurately known. The compound is then separated with the choice of the separation process being determined more by final purity rather than by quantitative recovery. The separated sample is weighed and its specific activity accurately determined. For beta emitters, the original and final samples should be counted in as similar a fashion as possible. If A_i and A_f are the specific activity of the added compound and of the final sample, respectively, and W_f is the weight of the final sample, then the weight of the compound in the original mixture, designated W_i, is given by

$$W_i = \left[\frac{A_i}{A_f} - 1\right] W_f$$

It may be more convenient to determine the amount of separated compound by some analytical means other than weighing so that 100% purity is unnecessary, but this in no way affects the principle of the technique. Isotope dilution is used to greatest advantage for organic mixtures where quantitative separation of the desired component is not feasible because of the presence of interfering compounds. The radioactivity is in reality a means of evaluating the chemical yield in the separation from these other substances.

This basic technique may not be directly applicable if an active sample of the pure compound is difficult or impossible to obtain, or no desirable

isolation procedure is known for the compound, or the amount of the compound in the mixture is very small. In such cases it is possible to use one of a number of variations of the isotope dilution technique. These usually involve preparing a derivative of the compound under analysis and then isolating and analyzing for the derivative. This is particularly valuable if the derivative is easily isolatable in a rather pure state. After formation of the derivative, a small amount of chemically identical, labeled derivative is added and the separation performed. The procedure after formation of the derivative is identical to that of normal isotope dilution. In all techniques using derivative formation, the derivative must be formed in high and reproducible yield and should be relatively stable throughout the isolation procedure.

In another variation of this method, the derivative is formed using a radioactive reagent. By accurate determination of the specific activity of the reagent and the isolated derivative, it should be possible to calculate the amount of unknown in the original mixture. If this amount is quite small, it may be advisable to use separation methods such as paper chromatography. If several compounds in the original mixture form similar derivatives, a chromatogram may allow simultaneous determination of their amounts, provided the R_f values are sufficiently different.

To avoid working on a microchemical level, it is often preferable in the cases of sub-microgram levels to add inactive carrier after formation of the active derivative. The labeled derivative and the added carrier are chemically identical. In the final sample the activity comes only from the unknown while the mass is attributable to the added carrier. Therefore, determination of the count rate and amount of derivative present after isolation, together with knowledge of the specific activity of the reagent and the amount of carrier added allows calculation of the quantity of unknown in the mixture. This procedure is capable of excellent sensitivity and, since it allows operation on a macro, or semimicro scale, it is usually to be recommended. A wide choice of active reagents are available from several chemical concerns. In the last chapter the use of I^{131} labeled *p*-iodobenzenesulfonyl chloride (pipsyl chloride) with the amino acids was described. With organic acids, C^{14} labeled diazomethane forms methyl esters. These acids may also be converted to active metal salts (e.g. with Co^{60}). For compounds with conjugated double bonds, labeled maleic anhydride has been shown to be a suitable reagent.

Radiometric Analysis

In inorganic systems, quantitative analysis may be performed by formation of an insoluble radioactive compound. The simplest technique is to add a slight excess of active reagent to the solution, quantitatively precipitating the unknown. The active precipitate is filtered, washed, and counted.

From knowledge of the specific activity of the reagent and the sample count rate, the amount present of the unknown may be calculated. Weighing is eliminated so chemical purity is unnecessary although radiochemical purity is very important. As a result, the sample may be quite small, it can be washed with weak salt solutions to prevent colloid formation, and any residual water or coprecipitated solids do not interfere in the analysis, provided the amount is insufficient to cause significant radiation absorption losses. The principal disadvantage of this method is that the error cannot be less than the counting error which is usually of the order of 0.5%.

More accurate methods involve counting aliquots of the filtrate. However, for very insoluble precipitates, this may require an appreciably higher total amount of radioactivity. If the stoichiometric endpoint is passed slightly by comparison of the specific activity of the filtrate (in cpm per ml) with that of the reagent solution (also in cpm per ml), the amount of excess reagent is calculated. It is a simple matter to calculate the amount of unknown after this. Reconsideration of Experiment 34 will point up the necessity of preventing an increase in solubility of the precipitate due to a salt effect by too great an excess of reagent. It may be necessary to include a correction in the calculations for the activity in the filtrate due to the slight solubility of the precipitate.

A variation of this technique involves adding identical aliquots of the unknown solution to a series of test tubes. Different aliquots of the reagent solution are then added to the tubes and after coagulation and centrifugation, an aliquot from each tube is removed and counted. The result is a

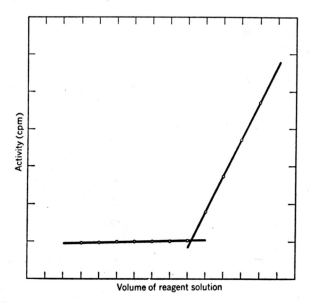

Figure 2. Titration curve, using radiometric analysis.

series of points on a titration curve (Figure 2) allowing determination of the end point. The same result is obtainable in a normal titration system in which, after each addition, a small filtered aliquot of the solution is removed, counted and returned to the titration vessel. For gamma emitters, this is very convenient as the liquid sample may be withdrawn through a sintered glass filter stick and counted in a well-scintillation counter. For beta emitters, a dipping Geiger-Müller tube is recommended. The count rate remains quite low until excess reagent is present, after which it steadily increases. In cases where visual indicators are of no use, such as in turbid or colored solutions or for very dilute solutions, this technique is of considerable merit.

It is also possible to add to the unknown solution a small amount of an active isotope, then titrate with an inactive reagent. The amount of activity in the supernatant liquid steadily decreases until the endpoint is reached, after which it has a constant, low value. The choice between labeled unknown or labeled reagent will probably be based on which is the more available.

EXPERIMENT 35

Quantitative Analysis for Zn

Purpose:

To study a simple technique of quantitative analysis using radioactive reagents.

Method:

(1) Prepare 5 ml of 0.10 M $(NH_4)_2HPO_4$ solution. Add approximately 15,000 cpm of P^{32} to the $(NH_4)_2HPO_4$ solution. Be certain that the solution is basic to phenolphthalein. The molarity of this solution must be known very accurately.

(2) To a 15 ml test tube, add exactly 1.00 ml of an unknown Zn^{2+} solution which is approximately 0.05 M in Zn. If a 1000 microliter pipet is used, it is calibrated "to contain" so it should be rinsed once with 1 M HCl and the rinsing added to the original volume. Add 2 drops of methyl orange; if the solution is not already acid, add concentrated HCl until it is acid. Then add 4 M NH$_4$OH dropwise until the solution is basic. Finally, add dilute (0.5 M) HCl dropwise until the solution just turns acid. Dilute the solution to approximately 5 ml with distilled water and heat almost to boiling in a beaker of hot water on a hot plate.

(3) Slowly add approximately 2 ml of the $(NH_4)_2HPO_4$ solution to the hot Zn solution to precipitate $ZnNH_4PO_4$. Continue heating until the pre-

cipitate becomes crystalline and settles rapidly. Remove the tube from the hot water bath and cool in an ice bath. Then filter the solution through one of the filter assemblies which the instructor will have set up. Wash the precipitate with 3 washes of 0.5 ml of cold 0.1 M $(NH_4)_2HPO_4$ solution *which contains no* P^{32}. Then follow with an ethyl alcohol and an acetone wash. Carefully remove the precipitate cake and filter paper and gently dry under a heat lamp. Tape a wide piece of Scotch tape across the bottom of a sample holder and place the filter paper on it. Across the top place a piece of thin cellophane and tape it to the holder along the edges but don't tape over the sample area. In all manipulations take care not to dislodge the precipitate. Be certain that all $(NH_4)_2HPO_4$ solutions are basic immediately prior to use as the pH may decrease on standing. A small quantity of phenolphthalein indicator in the solution provides a simple visual check.

(4) Prepare two samples of the P^{32} tracer on cellophane taped to a sample holder for counting in the same manner as the unknown. To do this evaporate 250 microliters of the tracer solution on the cellophane, then tape another piece of cellophane over the top.

(5) Count each sample for 5 minutes in a Geiger-Müller counter, then take a 5 minute background count. If the instructor so directs, run duplicate samples of the Zn unknown.

Data:

Calculate the specific activity (cpm per mg P) in the $(NH_4)_2HPO_4$ solution. From this data and the unknown count rate, calculate the Zn solution concentration. Calculate the standard deviation error of your answer from the counting error involved.

PROBLEMS

1. Would complete exchange be expected within 1 hour at room temperature between members of the following pairs? If exchange occurs even very slowly, suggest a reasonable mechanism.

    (a) Ag^{*+}, $AgCl$ (*s*)
    (b) Cr^{++}, Cr^{*+++}
    (c) $Cr^{*}O_4^{-}$, CrO_4^{-}
    (d) NH_4^+, D^+
    (e) $Fe(CN)_6^{3-}$, Fe^{*3+}

2. One millimole of a compound with the empirical formula MCl_3 is dissolved in an aqueous solution containing 1 milliequivalent of radioactive Cl^-. At intervals, samples of the compound are isolated from aliquots of the solution. After a very short interval, $\frac{2}{3}$ of the total activity becomes associated with the compound. Thereafter, the activity of the compound increases slowly until it reaches $\frac{3}{4}$ of the total activity. What is the simplest molecular formula consistent with these data? If the original specific activity of the Cl^- was 1000 cpm per mg of $AgCl$, what will be its final specific activity?

3. A 2.0 ml sample of an aqueous solution containing 0.1 microcurie per ml of tritium is injected into the blood stream of an animal. After allowing sufficient time for complete circulatory mixing, a 1.0 ml aliquot of blood is removed and found to have an activity of 1480 dpm of tritium. From this, calculate the blood volume of the animal.

4. A Grignard reaction was run beginning with 1.55 gm of bromobenzene. After completion of reaction, 2.5×10^4 dpm of C^{14} labeled benzoic acid was added to the reaction mixture. The benzoic acid was extracted once with petroleum ether and the extract was found to have 55 mg of benzoic acid with a specific activity of 190 dpm per mg. What was the acid yield in the Grignard reaction?

5. A 0.1 gm sample of animal tissue was taken to analyze for histamine. After extraction of the histamine, it is reacted with I^{131} labeled pipsyl chloride reagent with a specific activity of 2×10^6 cpm per micromole. After removal of unreacted reagent, 3000 micromoles of unlabeled pipsylhistamine are added to the mixture. After purification by recrystallization a 300 micromole (33 mg) sample was found to contain 400 cpm. What was the amount of histamine in the sample?

6. A reaction mixture containing butyl alcohol was reacted with excess C^{14} labeled acetic anhydride which had an activity of 5000 cpm per mg. The butyl acetate was isolated and found to have a total activity of 3.4×10^4 cpm. Calculate the amount of butyl alcohol in the reaction mixture.

7. A 1 ml sample of a solution containing trace amounts of lead and bismuth was subjected to paper chromatography in alcoholic hydrochloric acid solution. After development of the chromatogram, the wet strip was exposed to S^{35} labeled hydrogen sulfide gas whose activity was 2×10^5 cpm per microgram. Upon drying and counting the strip, a spot corresponding to the R_f value of lead was found to have an activity of 1900 cpm while a second at the correct position for bismuth was found to have 475 cpm. What are the concentrations of lead and bismuth per liter in the solution?

8. A 10 ml sample of an unknown Ba(II) solution was titrated by addition of a 0.010 M sulfate solution containing 100,000 cpm per ml; 100 microliter additions were made and a filtered aliquot counted after each addition. No significant counts were observed until the 6th addition when 235 cpm were obtained; subsequent 100 μl additions gave the following count rates in the solution aliquot: 1170, 2080, 2980 and 3860 cpm. What was the concentration of the barium solution?

REFERENCES

Exchange Reactions

Basolo, F., and R. G. Pearson, *Mechanisms of Inorganic Reactions*. New York: John Wiley & Sons, Inc., 1958.

Wahl, A. C., and N. A. Bonner, *Radioactivity Applied to Chemistry*. New York: John Wiley & Sons, Inc., 1951.

Determination of Ionic Charge

Martell, A. E., and M. Calvin, *Chemistry of the Metal Chelate Compounds*. Englewood Cliffs, N. J.: Prentice-Hall, Inc., 1952.

Solubility Studies

Glasstone, S., *Textbook of Physical Chemistry*. New York: D. Van Nostrand Co., Inc., 1946.

Hamill, W. H., and R. R. Williams, *Principles of Physical Chemistry*. Englewood Cliffs, N. J.: Prentice-Hall, Inc., 1959.

Analytical Radiochemistry

Cabell, M. J., and A. A. Smales, *Research* (London), **9**, 214 (1956).

Rodden, C. J., *Ann. Rev. Nuclear Sci.*, **1**, 343 (1952).

Technical Bulletins of the Nuclear-Chicago Corp.

General References on Radioisotope Uses

Edwards, R. R., *Ann. Rev. Nuclear Sci.*, **1**, 301 (1952).

Proceedings of the International Conference on the Peaceful Uses of Atomic Energy (Geneva: United Nations) Vol. 15 (1956).

XI

Tritium and Carbon-14

IN ORGANIC and biochemical systems, the most desirable radioactive tracers would be isotopes of H, C, N, and O. Unfortunately, only hydrogen and carbon have active isotopes of sufficiently long half life to be useful in experimentation. The two isotopes of importance are hydrogen-3 (tritium) and carbon-14. Both of these nuclides are beta emitters of low energy, and their importance makes it desirable to consider the modifications in counting technique connected with their use. Na^{22}, P^{32}, S^{35}, and I^{131} are some of the other nuclides of major importance in biochemical research, but of these only S^{35} requires special attention in counting.

The maximum beta energies for H^3 and C^{14} are 18 and 155 kev, respectively. Since the average beta energy has a value about one third as large as this maximum, the average energy is approximately 6 kev for H^3 and 50 kev for C^{14}. These energies correspond to half thickness values in aluminum of only 0.12 mg per cm^2 for tritium and 4.0 mg per cm^2 for C^{14}. The maximum beta energy in S^{35} is 167 kev ($d_{1/2}$ (Al) = 4.4 mg per cm^2) so the counting characteristics of S^{35} are similar to C^{14}. From Figure 2, Chapter V it can be ascertained that the transmission through a Geiger-Müller window of 1.4 mg per cm^2 thickness is 68% for C^{14} and 71% for S^{35}. If the window thickness is 4.0 mg per cm^2, the transmission is reduced to 38% for C^{14} and 42% for S^{35}. Even the 1.4 mg per cm^2 window is too thick to permit passage of the beta particles from tritium into the sensitive volume of the counter. For tritium it is necessary and for carbon-14 it is very useful to have beta absorption, whether by counter window or sample, reduced to an absolute minimum.

Since the radiations from H^3 and C^{14} are so soft, ingestion into the body represents the main danger to health. The radioactive half life is long but the biological half life is short for the major portion of the ingested sample. Some of the tracer may become rather permanently fixed in some part of the bone structure and at this position represents a long-term hazard. Inhalation and subsequent deposition in the lungs of insoluble compounds such as $BaCO_3$ is another method of establishment of a long-term radiation hazard. To avoid the possibility of ingestion, syntheses of and reactions with labeled compounds are conducted in closed systems under reduced pressure whenever possible. Frequently, as an additional safety precaution, these closed systems are set up in a high velocity radiochemical hood when an active gas such as CO_2 is involved.

Tritium

Tritium is produced in nuclear reactors by the reaction

$$Li^6 \ (n, \ \alpha)H^3$$

Conventional synthetic routes may be followed for the formation of tritium labeled compounds. However, in the case of very complex organic and biochemical molecules this may be quite time consuming and uneconomical if not impossible altogether. The Wilzbach method of tritiation involves the exposure of the unlabeled compound to a multicurie atmosphere of tritium gas for periods of time as long as two weeks. The decay of tritium during the exposure time results in ionization of the organic molecules. When this results in the rupture of a C—H bond, the molecule may capture a tritium atom in re-forming the bond. The result is labeling of the molecule. As might be evident, the process does not lead to labeling in one specific position. However, some positions will be labeled to a greater degree than others. For example, in toluene the per cent of total tritium incorporated at the various positions has been reported to be

While all the C—H bonds were susceptible to exchange, tritiation occurred more readily at the ortho position than the meta or para, and all the ring positions were more susceptible than the methyl group. In general, tritiation will occur most readily at the site of an active hydrogen in an organic molecule. Since radiation degradation also occurs during the exposure period, it is usually necessary to purify the desired labeled compound before use.

There is one very important precaution to be observed in using tritium labeled compounds. Labile tritium atoms undergo exchange with hydrogen in hydroxylic solvents. Consequently, reliable tracer studies with tritiated compounds in such solvents can be performed only with compounds which have no labile tritium atoms. This lability is connected with active hydrogen sites where the highest percentage of labeling occurs in the Wilzbach method. The labile tritiums may be removed by dissolution in a hydroxylic solvent before use of the labeled compound in an experimental system. In the same fashion the experimenter using tritium must be aware of the possibility of significant isotope effects due to the large mass difference between H^1 and H^3. For carbon-hydrogen bonds, the C—H^3 bond is a little less labile than the C—H^1 bond. This is a result of the lower zero point vibrational energy of the C—H^3 bond which results in a larger heat of activation for rupture of the bond.

Tritium is counted most frequently in the gaseous form as H_2 or as a light hydrocarbon. Oxidation of labeled organic compounds yields tritiated water, which in turn can be reacted with active metals to form H_2. The problems of introduction of the gas into a Geiger-Müller or proportional counting tube or into an ion chamber are similar to those discussed for C^{14} in the next section. Liquid scintillation counting techniques are rapidly increasing in importance for tritium.

Carbon-14

Carbon-14 is prepared in nuclear reactors by the reaction

$$N^{14}\ (n, p)C^{14}$$

An unusual aspect of this reaction is that it can occur with thermal neutrons. Normally, the coulomb barrier of the nucleus is too large to permit evaporation of protons by the binding energy released upon absorption by the nucleus of a thermal neutron. Although the half life of C^{14} is only 5568 years, the carbon compounds in the atmosphere and in living systems have some C^{14} in them. This is a result of the reaction of neutrons on atmospheric nitrogen and occurs in the atmosphere as a result of cosmic rays. Carbon in living systems will have the same specific activity for C^{14} as the CO_2 in the air. Death destroys the equilibrium with atmospheric CO_2 necessary to maintain the constancy in the specific activity, and measurement of the specific activity allows evaluation of the period of time which has elapsed since death. Libby and others have developed this C^{14} dating method into a major archeological tool.

Many C^{14} labeled compounds are available commercially. These may be used directly or as a reactant in preparation of another labeled product. If the experiment involves following the behavior of the labeled molecule through a chemical or physical process which does not degrade the molecule, the site of labeling is not important. However, if decomposition occurs, it is necessary that the labeled site be connected with the functional group or the molecular fragment being studied in the process. If the labeled compound is the end product of a multistep synthesis, in order to obtain a higher final yield, it is best to achieve the labeling at as late a point in the synthesis as possible. It is a recommended procedure to conduct several practice runs of the synthesis before use of C^{14}. This ensures consideration of all factors in equipment, conditions, and technique necessary for successful and safe experimentation with tracers.

Most syntheses of C^{14} labeled organic compounds follow conventional routes with some modifications to increase yield and to decrease the scale of operations for lower amounts of reactants and products. Carbon dioxide gas liberated by action of a strong acid on $BaCO_3$ is frequently used for labeling syntheses. $BaCO_3$ can be the starting material for syntheses using acetylene, also. The following reactions illustrate the synthesis of labeled acetic acid as a typical example.

(A) Acetic Acid-2-C^{14}.

$$BaC^*O_3 \xrightarrow{HCl} C^*O_2 \xrightarrow[\text{catalyst}]{H_2} C^*H_3OH \xrightarrow{PI_3} C^*H_3I \xrightarrow{KCN} C^*H_3CN$$

$$C^*H_3CO_2H \xleftarrow{H_2O} $$

(B) Acetic Acid-1-C^{14}.

$$BaC^*O_3 \xrightarrow{HCl} C^*O_2 \xrightarrow{CH_3MgBr} CH_3C^*O_2H$$

(C) Acetic Acid-1,2-C^{14}.

$$BaC^*O_3 \xrightarrow[\text{Mg}]{\Delta} BaC^*_2 \xrightarrow{H_2O} C^*_2H_2 \xrightarrow[\text{catalyst}]{H_2O} C^*H_3C^*HO$$

$$C^*H_3C^*O_2H \xleftarrow{[O]} $$

Alternately,

$$KC^*N \xrightarrow{C^*H_3I} C^*H_3C^*N \xrightarrow{H_2O} C^*H_3C^*O_2H$$

Calvin, *et al.*,[1] have described in detail many organic syntheses with carbon-14.

---

[1] Calvin, Heidelberger, Reid, Tolbert, and Yankwich, *Isotopic Carbon* (New York: John Wiley & Sons, Inc., 1949).

The first step in preparation of a counting sample consists in oxidation of the organic compound with the evolution of active carbon dioxide. Dry combustion in quartz tubes may be used, but more often oxidation is effected in solution by strong chemical oxidizing mixtures. A solution mixture of CrO_3, KIO_3, H_3PO_4 and fuming H_2SO_4, first used by Van Slyke and Folch, is capable of excellent results. The oxidation is complete in a few minutes, and the CO_2 may be condensed from the gas system in a trap immersed in liquid nitrogen. The CO_2 is dried before condensation by passage through a trap immersed in a dry ice-acetone bath (Figure 1). In order to avoid fractionation through isotope effects, the combustion should be quantitative.

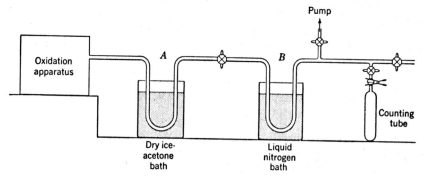

Figure 1. Gas system for C^{14} sample oxidation to CO_2 and for filling gas counting tube.

If a solid counting sample is desired, the gaseous CO_2 is absorbed in an alkaline solution and precipitated as $BaCO_3$. If a quantitative determination of the CO_2 is desired, it is essential that the alkaline solution be as carbonate free as possible. Insoluble carbonates of lighter metals would have relatively less sample self-absorption, but only $BaCO_3$ possesses desirable coagulation properties. The $BaCO_3$ precipitate may be evaporated to dryness from an aqueous slurry or may be filtered. In evaporation, the $BaCO_3$ may lose some activity as a result of exchange with atmospheric CO_2. This is particularly true if the evaporating solution is acidic as the exchange takes place via the intermediation of H_2CO_3.

The $BaCO_3$ solid samples are counted by the use of end window Geiger-Müller and thin window or windowless proportional counters. Since the beta energy is so low, sample self-absorption is a major factor in establishing the count rate which is observed. For quantitative measurements two methods are used, and in both it is necessary that the experimental counting arrangement be reproduced very closely for all samples. In the first method, the count rate is determined as a function of the density (in mg per cm^2) of the sample. Then, the specific activity of the sample without

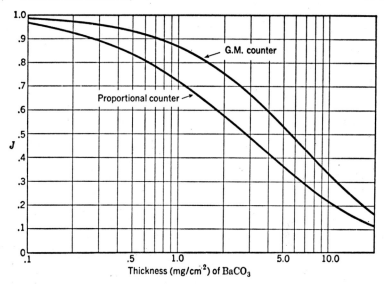

Figure 2. The self-absorption factor J for $BaCO_3$ samples of C^{14}.

self-absorption losses may be calculated using the proper correction factor. This latter is determined for $BaCO_3$ with the same experimental counting arrangement (see Experiment 7, Chapter V).

The second technique involves counting cf infinitely thick samples. When the sample is thicker than the range R of C^{14} betas, it is considered to be infinitely thick as only those beta rays originating within the thickness R can leave the surface. In practice, the thickness need only exceed 20% of the value of the total range for the sample to be infinitely thick. It is critical that the samples all be of uniform distance from the counter window and of constant area. If it is necessary to add additional inactive carbonate to obtain the infinitely thick deposit, care must be taken that the sample is of uniform composition and specific activity throughout. Since, for a series of thick samples of uniform area, the same upper portion contributes to the observed count rate, the count rate is proportional to the specific activity of the sample. It is unnecessary to use any correction factors as this technique allows direct comparison of specific activities between the samples.

Liquid scintillation counting techniques are increasingly important for soft beta emitters such as H^3, C^{14}, and S^{35}. The radioactive material may be dissolved in the scintillating liquid or ground into a fine powder and a uniform suspension formed. The latter may be easier to achieve for polar compounds than solution in the scintillating liquid. For suspensions a uniform, reproducible grain size must be achieved which represents an infinite thickness for the beta emitter or, alternately, an internal standard whose state of dispersion is the same as that of the unknown must be added

to the mixture. Self-absorption critically reduces the counting efficiency for tritium unless extremely small grain size is achieved, and, consequently, the attractiveness of the suspension technique for tritium containing materials is somewhat reduced. In addition to the ease of preparation, suspension counting has the advantages (over solution counting) of recovery of the active material by filtration and of absence of quenching problems common to solution counting. Of course, it is necessary to ensure uniformity in the suspension and to prevent settling. One method of stabilizing suspensions involves addition of a substance which causes a gel to form as the temperature is lowered. A finely divided preparation of silicon dioxide, Cab-O-Sil, has been used in this manner to form an optically clear, thixotropic system of suspensions of dry powders and aqueous solutions in scintillating liquids.[2] The reported efficiency is 65% for C^{14} and 14% for H^3 suspensions.

Toluene and xylene are popular as the bulk solvent of the scintillating liquid. As the soluble scintillator, p-terphenyl or 2.5-diphenyl-oxazole (PPO) is used in a concentration of approximately 4g/l. Usually an additional solute is added to function as a wave length shifter. In concentrations of 0.05-0.1g/l 1,4-bis(2-(5-phenyloxazole)-benzene) (POPOP) serves to absorb the primary photon emissions and to re-emit light at wave lengths closer to those necessary for optimum operation of the photomultiplier tube. For solutions of active samples, it is often necessary to add an additional component such as ethanol to this system to increase its polar character. These substances, as well as the dissolved active compounds, may serve to quench the scintillation process, reducing the counting efficiency.

There are a number of things which can be done to increase the counting efficiency and to reduce the background. The photomultiplier tubes are chosen for optimum signal-to-noise ratio so that thermionic noise does not obscure the counting pulses. This noise is further suppressed by operation of the counting process at low temperatures. In commercial liquid scintillation counting units, the samples and photomultiplier are placed in a freezer. In addition, two photomultiplier tubes are operated in coincidence to reduce the background. Further reduction is effected by using solvents of petrochemical origin, thereby eliminating natural C^{14} background. In the external electronic circuitry, pulse-height discrimination can be used to reject noise pulses and gamma-ray background pulses.

Gas-phase counting is in common usage for C^{14} measurements. It has the advantage of very nearly 100% geometry with no sample self-absorption or window absorption losses. The C^{14} is prepared for counting by formation of CO_2, CH_4, or C_2H_2. For Geiger-Müller counting, CO_2 can be mixed with the counting gas only in relatively small amounts. This fact and the sensitivity to impurities make Geiger-Müller counting less attrac-

[2] C. F. Gordon, and A. L. Wolfe, *Anal. Chem.*, **32**, 574 (1960).

tive than proportional counting. For the latter, the low beta energy makes it necessary to have greater than normal electronic amplification. However, much higher levels of specific activity may be counted with no resolving time losses. The counter tube is filled with the active sample from the gas system by immersing the tube in liquid nitrogen (see Figure 1). As CO_2, C^{14} can be counted in an ionization chamber which is connected to a vibrating reed electrometer. This last system is capable of handling relatively large volumes (10 millimoles) of CO_2 and is one of the simplest and yet most accurate methods of detecting radiation.

Experimental

In Experiment 36 it is important that the reaction mixture in flask *A* be stirred, otherwise C^*O_2 evolution is not quantitative and a large fraction of the C^*O_2 is found in the liquid air trap. Also, the maximum capacity of the system for CO_2 should be determined before the active $BaCO_3$ run. This can be done by first performing the experiment with inactive $BaCO_3$.

As an example of carbon-14 labeling, Experiment 37 describes the synthesis of benzoic acid by the Grignard reaction with active CO_2. Since both O_2 and H_2O decompose the Grignard reagent, they should be excluded from the system. In this experiment, oxygen causes formation of phenol which is difficult subsequently to separate from the benzoic acid. The concentration of the Grignard reagent is kept below 0.5 M to ensure complete solubility during the reaction. Agitation and a low temperature minimizes by-product formation of carbinols and ketones.

As an additional experiment, the preparation of uniform samples of BaC^*O_3 may be assigned. The BaC^*O_3 should be placed in an agate mortar with a little alcohol and ground. The slurry is allowed to settle for a few seconds, then transferred to a cup planchet and carefully evaporated to dryness under a heat lamp. By preparation of samples with different amounts of inactive $BaCO_3$, a self-absorption curve may be run for BaC^*O_3. The student should practice preparation of inactive samples of $BaCO_3$ initially as there is danger of spreading active BaC^*O_3 dust in these operations. For this same reason, this experiment should be performed only in a good hood.

If the equipment is available, it is recommended that an experiment be conducted wherein a sample of C^*O_2 is counted in an ionization chamber-electrometer apparatus. Sulfuric acid may be added to BaC^*O_3 to generate the C^*O_2 which is then drawn into a previously evacuated ionization chamber in a manner described in connection with Figure 1. Alternately, a sample of a C^{14} labeled organic compound may be oxidized by the Van Slyke technique and counted in the ionization chamber-electrometer apparatus (or the C^*O_2 is absorbed in alkaline solution and precipitated as BaC^*O_3 prior to Geiger-Müller or proportional counting).

The benzoic acid-C¹⁴ prepared in Experiment 37 may be used in this oxidation.

The Preparation of Sodium Carbonate—C-14

Purpose:

To prepare $Na_2C^{14}O_3$ from $BaC^{14}O_3$.

Method:

Figure 3 is a diagram of the experimental arrangement. A sample of active $BaCO_3$ is added to flask A along with a magnetic stirring bar. A

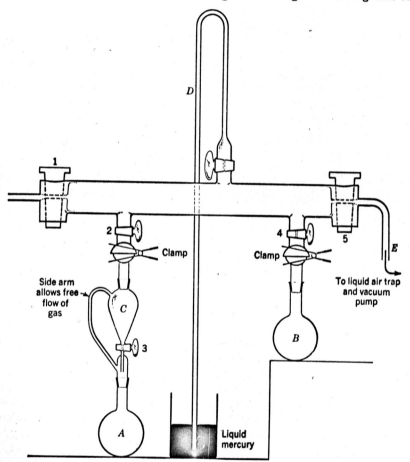

Figure 3. Experimental arrangement for preparation of $Na_2C^*O_3$ from BaC^*O_3. All joints are of ground-glass.

volume of concentrated H_2SO_4 in slight stoichiometric excess to the $BaC*O_3$ sample is placed in the separatory funnel C and both A and C are connected to the manifold with stopcocks 2 and 3 closed. 5 ml of NaOH solution of sufficient concentration to be in slight excess to the $BaC*O_3$ is added to flask B. The NaOH solution is frozen by immersion of B in a dry ice-acetone bath, then B is attached to the manifold line. With stopcocks 1 and 3 closed and 2, 4, 5, and 6 open, the system is evacuated through E. The Hg column in D should rise to a height of at least 75 cm. After evacuation, 5 is closed and the NaOH solution allowed to melt by removal of the cold bath from B. Then with the magnetic stirrer on, the H_2SO_4 is allowed to drip slowly on the $BaC*O_3$ by opening 3 slightly. A drop in the Hg level is evidence of evolution of $C*O_2$. After completion of the $C*O_2$ evolution, the Hg level should rise again as the $C*O_2$ is absorbed by the NaOH solution. If the system is without leaks, the final level should be the same as before initiation of the gas evolution. Flask A may be heated slightly to insure liberation of all the $C*O_2$. Upon completion of the evolution and absorption, 4 and 6 are closed and upon opening 5, the system is subjected to pumping. Stopcock 1 is opened slightly to allow air to be swept through the system by the pumping. Any residual $C*O_2$ is trapped in the liquid air trap. This latter should be able to be isolated from the system by stopcocks and while the $C*O_2$ is still frozen, NaOH solution is added to the trap to prevent escape of active $C*O_2$.

Data:

Count aliquot samples of the Na_2C*O_3 and from the total volume of solution calculate the total C^{14} activity present. Compare with the original sample to obtain a yield.

EXPERIMENT 37

Preparation of Benzoic Acid—C-14

Purpose:

To study the synthesis of a C^{14} labeled organic compound.

Method:

The experimental apparatus is assembled as in Figure 4. 2.65 gm of Na_2CO_3 and 100 microliters of $Na_2C^{14}O_3$ is placed in flask A. An equivalent amount of inactive $BaCO_3$ and an equal activity of C^{14} as $BaC^{14}O_3$ may be used. The total C^{14} activity is ascertained by counting a small aliquot in a proportional counter—10^4 to 10^6 cpm is a good range. Concentrated H_2SO_4 (HCl for $BaCO_3$) is placed in the separatory funnel B in an amount

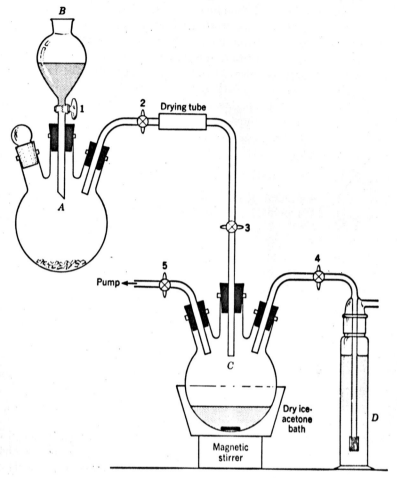

Figure 4. Experimental arrangement for the synthesis of benzoic
acid—C^{14}.

in stoichiometric excess of the Na$_2$CO$_3$ sample. A Grignard solution is
prepared in flask C from 0.6 gm magnesium turnings and 3.9 gm of bromobenzene in 75 ml of absolute diethyl ether and stirred magnetically.
Stopcocks 1 and 4 are closed and 2, 3, and 5 opened and the system evacuated with an oil pump until the ether begins to boil. Then 5 is closed and
1 is opened cautiously to admit the acid into flask A. When nearly all the
acid has been added to A, C is immersed in a dry ice-acetone bath to
insure condensation of the C*O$_2$ into the Grignard solution. Warm flask A
to complete the C*O$_2$ evolution. Allow some air into the system through B
to sweep all the C*O$_2$ into C. Continue stirring the contents of C throughout
the experiment. Close all stopcocks and allow the system to stir overnight,

during which time the dry ice sublimes and the system reaches room temperature. Then, bring the system to atmospheric pressure by opening 1, 2, and 3. Expel excess C^*O_2 by air flow through a NaOH solution in D. Extract the benzoic acid from the ether with aqueous NaOH solution, then precipitate it by addition of a slight excess of 6 M HCl. Precipitate any $C^*O_3^=$ in the NaOH with Ba^{++}.

The benzoic acid sample is dissolved in ether and the solution brought to a volume of 25 ml in a volumetric flask. An aliquot of this solution is removed, evaporated to dryness on a counting planchet, and counted in the proportional counter.

Data:

Write equations for all the reactions involved. Calculate the yield of benzoic acid.

EXPERIMENT 38

Studies with Labeled Benzoic Acid

Purpose:

To use benzoic acid-C^{14} to study liquid-liquid extraction purification and isotope dilution.

Method:

A. Use the ether solution of labeled benzoic acid from Experiment 37. Adjust the concentration of a portion with inactive benzoic acid so that 5 ml of solution contains 20 mg of benzoic acid (with an activity level of 10^4-10^5 cpm C^{14}). To a 25 ml separatory funnel, add 5 ml of the benzoic acid solution, 2.5 ml of H_2O and 2.5 ml of absolute ethyl alcohol. Stopper the funnel and shake vigorously for 30 seconds, then allow the layers to separate. Remove the bottom phase which is the 50% alcoholic solution. Take a 2 ml aliquot of this solution, add 100 mg of inactive benzoic acid and evaporate slowly to dryness on a counting planchet. Carefully smooth the dried deposit, if necessary, to obtain an even deposit. Repeat this exact procedure with a 2 ml aliquot of the ether phase. Count both samples in the proportional counter or with exactly duplicated conditions with a thin window Geiger-Müller counter.

Data:

Calculate the per cent benzoic acid in each phase and the concentration in mg per ml in each phase. Calculate a distribution ratio D for this system.

Method:

B. Obtain from the instructor a crude mixture of organic compounds containing some benzoic acid. Add a known amount (approximately 10^5 cpm) of labeled benzoic acid from Experiment 37 whose specific activity is well known. Dissolve the mixture in hydrochloric acid and extract with ether. Purify the benzoic acid by successive recrystallizations to a constant melting point. Determine the sample weight. Then prepare a sample to be counted in the same fashion as the one which is used to determine the specific activity of the added benzoic acid-C^{14} sample.

Data:

Calculate the specific activity of the final sample. Use the considerations in Chapter X on the isotope dilution technique to calculate the percentage of benzoic acid in the original sample.

REFERENCES

Aronoff, S., *Techniques of Radiobiochemistry*. Ames, Iowa: Iowa State College Press, 1956.

Burr, J. G., Jr., *Tracer Application for the Study of Organic Reactions*. New York: Interscience Publishers, Inc., 1957.

Bradford, J. R., *Radioisotopes in Industry*. New York: Reinhold Publishing Corp., 1953.

Calvin, et al., *Isotopic Carbon*. New York: John Wiley & Sons, Inc., 1949.

Kamen, M. D., *Radioactive Tracers in Biology*. New York: Academic Press, 1948.

Libby, W. F., *J. Chem. Educ.*, **34**, 578 (1957).

Overman, R. T., and H. M. Clark, *Radioisotope Techniques*. New York: McGraw-Hill Book Co., Inc., 1960.

Proceedings of the Symposium on Advances in Tracer Applications of Tritium. New York, 1958. Copies may be obtained from the New England Nuclear Corp., 575 Albany St., Boston 18, Mass.

Robinson, R. H., *J. Chem. Educ.*, **32**, 370 (1955).

Sulfur-35 Counting

Jeffay, Olubaja, and Jewell, *Anal. Chem.*, **32**, 306 (1960).

Merritt, N. F., and Hawkings, R. C., *Anal. Chem.*, **32**, 308 (1960).

Merritt, Taylor, Merritt, and Campion, *Anal. Chem.*, **32**, 310 (1960).

XII

Radiation Chemistry

THE USE of the excitation and ionization arising from the interaction of radiation with matter to detect and study the characteristics of radiation has been discussed in earlier chapters. The objective of the field of radiation chemistry is the understanding of the physical and chemical changes which take place in the absorbing medium subsequent to the passage of the radiation. A few examples may serve to illustrate the importance of some knowledge of this field to everyone using or studying radioactivity. The organic chemist who intends to use a C^{14} labeled compound in mechanism experiments must be aware of the consequences of decomposition during storage in the organic sample as a result of the β emissions. The extent to which the internal irradiation by alpha particles causes reduction of plutonium ions to the (IV) state in an aqueous solution of PuO_2^{2+} is necessary knowledge for the inorganic chemist studying plutonyl ion chemistry. Nuclear engineers must understand the effects of prolonged subjection of all reactor materials to intense fluxes of neutrons and gamma rays.

Radiation Sources

Most of the early research in radiation chemistry used natural nuclear emissions. Now, a large variety of methods are available for the production

of intense fluxes of a wide assortment of radiation beams. Van de Graaff and linear accelerators may be purchased commercially which supply elec-trons with energies as high as 3–10 Mev. Positive ions (p^+, d^+, He^{+2}, C^{+6}) are obtainable in cyclotrons as well as Van de Graaff and linear accelera-tors. Neutrons and X rays are produced in the accelerators by electron or positive ion bombardment of suitable targets. The ability to hold the energy and area of irradiation constant is the principal advantage in the use of accelerators in radiation chemistry.

Figure 1. Van de Graaff electrostatic accelerator. (Photograph Courtesy of Florida State University)

Nuclear reactors supply large numbers of neutrons and have the advan-tages of being able to accommodate many samples up to quite large sizes and for considerable lengths of time. Nuclear reactor fuel elements, after completion of their useful life in a reactor, are excellent sources for high-level gamma irradiations. However, they have the disadvantage of pro-viding a spectrum of photon energies, and since both the intensity and the spectral distribution change with time in an almost unpredictable fashion, sources not possessing these disadvantages are favored for research use. Co^{60} sources prepared by neutron irradiation of Co^{59} in reactors are in widespread use.

General Considerations

It is tempting to seek to relate photochemistry and radiation chemistry by considering that ionization is the ultimate state of excitation. However, the occurrence of ionization in radiolysis with approximately equal partition of energy between ionization and excitation makes the system much more complicated, and the similarities to the results of photolysis are apt to be superficial.

The over-all radiation process may be separated into several steps. In its passage through the material the radiation induces ionization. The electrons from the primary ionization have sufficient kinetic energy to cause secondary ionization. The number of electrons from this additional ionization is larger than that from the primary ionization, but the kinetic energies are lower on the average. These secondary electrons collide with molecules, causing excitation to higher energy states. The excitation to these higher electronic and vibrational states, as discussed in Chapter VII, is followed by de-excitation by means of fluorescence, collisional transfer of energy, and various modes of molecular dissociation. Various molecular fragments existing as ions and radicals are the result of these ionizations and excitations.

In the secondary stage of the process, these species interact to produce neutral molecules, and new ions and radicals. Ion–molecule reactions of the type

$$AB^+ + CD = AC^+ + BD$$

occur quite generally. The electrons from the ionizations recombine either with positive ions or with species of high electron affinity. The combination process is frequently sufficiently exothermic to cause bond rupture, producing new ionic and radical species. Since in a gas the ionization density is relatively low compared to a condensed system, no matter what the type and energy of the radiation, the ions and radicals diffuse, and recombination occurs at distances remote from the sites of production. In condensed media, the increased collisional rate and the "cage effect" of the surrounding molecules result in a much more rapid removal of energy, and enhance the probability of recombination within the local volume. The concentration of ions and radicals in this local volume is a function of the ionization density. Therefore, the over-all effects are more dependent on the energy and type of the radiations in condensed media than in gases. In the case of dilute solutions, the solvent molecules absorb the radiation energy in the primary act. The effect on the solute can be understood by consideration of the probable reactions with the radiation products of the solvent. The autoreduction of PuO_2^{2+} in aqueous solution is an example of this type of secondary effect.

In the degradation of the kinetic energy of neutrons by nuclear collisions,

the recoiling atom has sufficient kinetic energy to break bonds. Products of nuclear reactions (see Chapter VIII) also possess enough recoil energy to effect bond rupture. These "hot atoms" rapidly lose their excess energy in a few collisions, and while still hot may have enough energy to undergo reactions which might normally be unlikely because of a large activation energy. Since this must occur within the first few collisions, the probability of hot atom reactions with other than a major component of the system is small. However, after thermalization the activation energy for reaction with the major component may be sufficiently large to prohibit reaction of the atoms with the major component. In these cases reaction with a minor component may be more likely if the activation energy is lower.

In order to gain some insight into how radiation chemists are able to understand some order in this apparent chaos, several particular systems are considered in the remainder of this chapter.

Radiolysis of Water

The first reaction in the irradiation of water is considered to be

$$H_2O \overset{\wedge\wedge\wedge}{\longrightarrow} H_2O^+ + e^- \qquad \text{(XII-1)}$$

where the symbol $\overset{\wedge\wedge\wedge}{\longrightarrow}$ signifies action by radiation. Two subsequent modes of reaction have been suggested. In one the electron is immediately recaptured and the excited molecule dissociates into radicals

$$H_2O^+ + e^- \longrightarrow H_2O^* \longrightarrow H + OH \qquad \text{(XII-2)}$$

The alternative mechanism for the production of H and OH radicals after reaction (1) is

$$H_2O^+ + H_2O \longrightarrow H_3O^+ + OH \qquad \text{(XII-3)}$$

$$e^- + H_2O \longrightarrow H_2O^- \longrightarrow H + OH^- \qquad \text{(XII-4)}$$

In heavy particle irradiation of water, the ionization density is high and the cage effect serves to cause the radicals to combine locally to form H_2 and H_2O_2. In electron and gamma irradiations, the lower ionization density allows greater radical diffusion away from the local volume. In solutions, then, the main effect on the solute in heavy ion bombardment is attack by H_2O_2 and H_2, whereas in electron or gamma irradiation the main effect is radical attack. In aerated solutions, HO_2 (the hydroperoxy radical), H_2^+ and O^- are species also present for solute attack. In very pure water, there is essentially no net decomposition with irradiation by gamma and X rays as a steady state is reached in which the water dissociates at a rate equal to reassociation via the reactions

$$H_2 + OH \longrightarrow H + H_2O \qquad \text{(XII-5)}$$

$$H + H_2O_2 \longrightarrow OH + H_2O \qquad \text{(XII-6)}$$

$$H + OH \longrightarrow H_2O \qquad \text{(XII-7)}$$

The presence of even small amounts of impurity, especially if it has a high affinity for radicals (a scavenger), causes decomposition by competing with the above reactions as follows

$$X^- + OH \longrightarrow X + OH^- \qquad \text{(XII-8)}$$

$$X + H \longrightarrow X^- + H^+ \qquad \text{(XII-9)}$$

Thus the radiolysis products, H_2 and H_2O_2 can increase in concentration. In nuclear reactors when water is used as a coolant or a moderator, it should be as pure as possible to minimize dissociation during the time in the reactor.

Radiolysis of Organic Systems

Organic molecules, in general, are more complicated species than the water molecule and hence, the radiolysis should be expected to give a greater variety of products. H_2, CO, CO_2, fragments smaller than the irradiated molecule and polymeric species are all produced in C, H, and O systems. In hydrocarbons both C—C and C—H bonds are severed. The presence of polymeric products such as C_3H_8 can not be explained readily by simple radical combination but rather are probably formed in ion-molecule reactions.

$$CH_4 \longrightarrow\!\!\!\wedge\!\!\wedge\!\!\wedge\!\!\!\longrightarrow CH_4^+ + e^- \qquad \text{(XII-10)}$$

$$CH_4^+ + CH_4 \longrightarrow CH_3 + CH_3^+ + H_2 \qquad \text{(XII-11)}$$

$$CH_3^+ + CH_4 \longrightarrow C_2H_5^+ + H_2 \qquad \text{(XII-12)}$$

$$C_2H_5^+ + CH_4 \longrightarrow C_3H_7^+ + H_2 \qquad \text{(XII-13)}$$

$$C_3H_7^+ + CH_4 \longrightarrow C_3H_8 + CH_3^+ \qquad \text{(XII-14)}$$

Upon irradiation with gamma rays from a Co^{60} source, the hydrogen yield from cyclohexane is 150 times greater than that from benzene. This has been interpreted to be a result of the greater stability of the excited states of aromatic systems which enhances the probability of dissipation of excitation energy by collisional transfers, thus decreasing the decomposition. Even aliphatic side chains show increased stability to hydrogen formation, presumably as a result of the transference of the excess energy to the ring before decomposition can occur. However, since the yield of polymeric products in the cyclohexane irradiation is only a little more than double that in the benzene irradiation, a full explanation of these differences may require a more subtle interpretation of the effect of aromaticity.

In some plastics, such as polyethylene, irradiation produces cross-linking of chains. Degradation of the main chain or of side chains is the major effect with other polymers.

Radiolysis of Solids

In Chapter VII, the effect of radiations on organic and inorganic crystals was considered. In addition to excitation followed by fluorescence, several other effects are quite important in heavy particle irradiations, particularly to the physical characteristics. Following a collision or ionization the recoiling ion produces lattice vacancies and upon stopping may occupy a non-equilibrium interstitial position. The localized dissipation of energy can result in lattice oscillations terminating in some reorientation of local regions in the crystal lattice. These crystal defects increase the energy content of the crystal. Semiconductors, where the concentration of charge carriers is very small, have their conductivity reduced by introduction of lattice defects during irradiation. The production of interstitial atoms in reactors makes the graphite stronger, harder, and more brittle. Of course, chemical decomposition effects are produced as well in solid systems by similar mechanisms to those discussed earlier.

Radiation Self-decomposition

Labeled compounds will undergo radiolysis induced by the labeling radioactivity. The effect of this radiation self-decomposition has been reviewed by Tolbert[1] for organic compounds. The extent of such radiation effects depends on the half life and the average radiation energy of the radioactivity, the specific activity of the sample, and the number of molecules permanently changed per 100 ev of energy absorbed. Of course, the presence of other substances can considerably affect the amount of damage. Aromatic compounds such as benzene (as a solvent) can serve as a protective medium to minimize radiation self-decomposition, whereas water or oxygen enhance it. For soft beta emitters such as H^3, C^{14}, and S^{35}, where the radiation path length is less than the sample dimensions, the radiation dose in rads for pure samples can be approximated fairly well by

$$\text{Radiation dose in rads} = \frac{N\bar{E}\,(1.6 \times 10^{-14})}{W} \qquad \text{(XII-15)}$$

where

N = number of beta particles,
$\bar{E}$ = average energy (in ev),
W = sample weight in grams.

$H^3 = 5700$ ev, $C^{14} = 45,000$ ev, $S^{35} = 50,000$ ev.

[1] B. M. Tolbert, *Atomlight*. New England Nuclear Corporation Publication, February, 1960.

Radiation doses of 10^7 rads can induce significant decomposition effects—of the order of one per cent. Samples whose specific activity exceed 1 millicurie per millimole for C^{14} or 8 millicuries per millimole for H^3 will receive a dose of this magnitude in a period of a year. Consequently, stored samples whose self-radiolysis dose has reached the level of 10^7 rads should be repurified before use if the decomposition products are likely to affect the experiment. Samples may be stored in benzene solution, in vacuo or in a deep freezer to minimize these self-radiation effects.

Dosimetry

An important requirement in the quantitative study of radiation effects is the ability to measure accurately the amount of energy given to the system. Techniques of physical dosimetry involving the measurement of the total ionization have been described in Chapter II. In many instances chemical dosimetry is preferred, wherein the amount of chemical change produced in a standard system is measured. The extent of the chemical effect must be proportional to the total radiation dose but not to the intensity or type of radiation. For a practical dosimeter, the system should have an easily measured effect using ordinary, stable reagents and should not be very sensitive to impurities.

The ferrous sulfate dosimeter (Experiment 39) has been studied thoroughly and comes very close to fulfilling all these requirements. In this system, the oxidation of Fe(II) to Fe(III) is studied in dilute sulfuric acid. The advantage of being able to use the system in the presence of oxygen serves to overcome its two main disadvantages, a relatively high sensitivity to impurities and the difficulty in measuring effects for doses below 5000 roentgens. The reactions subsequent to the formation of H and OH radicals are

$$\text{Fe(II)} + \text{OH} \longrightarrow \text{Fe(III)} + \text{OH}^- \qquad \text{(XII-16)}$$

$$\text{H} + \text{O}_2 \longrightarrow \text{HO}_2 \qquad \text{(XII-17)}$$

$$\text{H}^+ + \text{HO}_2 + \text{Fe(II)} \longrightarrow \text{H}_2\text{O}_2 + \text{Fe(III)} \qquad \text{(XII-18)}$$

$$\text{Fe(II)} + \text{H}_2\text{O}_2 \longrightarrow \text{Fe(III)} + \text{OH} + \text{OH}^- \qquad \text{(XII-19)}$$

Since this last hydroxy radical reacts by Equation (XII-16), four Fe(II) ions are oxidized by the radicals. The H_2O_2 present due to radical combination also reacts via Equation (XII-19) to oxidize Fe(II). A value of 15.5 has been determined by many investigators for the number of ferrous ions oxidized per 100 ev of radiation energy absorbed. The number of molecules (or radicals) destroyed or produced per 100 ev of energy absorbed is the unit of radiation effects and is known as the G value. A G value may be expressed for each species formed or destroyed in any system. Since the $G\{\text{Fe(II)}\} = 15.5$ for the ferrous sulfate dosimeter, if the total concentra-

tion of Fe(III) after irradiation is determined, the total energy deposited may be calculated quite easily.

Other chemical dosimeters are in use, and in all cases the radiation dose necessary to obtain a measurable reaction is rather sizable. Gas evolution dosimetry has been used to measure gamma and neutron fluxes. Usually an aqueous solution of potassium iodide is used, and the result is the evolution of hydrogen and oxygen in a 2:1 molar ratio after attainment of steady-state conditions.

Experimental

Experiment 39 is written for measurement of the dose rate of a Co^{60} source. However, it may be easily modified for use with an accelerator or reactor if this is desired.

In the radiolysis of alkyl iodides, the C—I bond is broken in preference to any C—H bonds. In pure methyl iodide the principal products are ethane and iodine with lower yields of methane and methylene diiodide. In contrast to this, in photolysis these latter two compounds are the major products, while ethane and iodine are produced in lower yields. The presence in radiolysis of ion-molecule as well as radical reactions explains this difference between the radiolysis and the photolysis yields.

EXPERIMENT 39

Chemical Dosimetry[2]

Purpose:

To prepare a simple chemical system to measure the radiation dose.

Method:

Prepare a 1000 ml of solution containing

> 0.40 g $FeSO_4 \cdot 7H_2O$ or $Fe(NH_4)_2(SO_4)_2 \cdot 6H_2O$
> 0.06 g NaCl
> 22 ml of concentrated H_2SO_4 (95–98%)

The chloride ions inhibit oxidation of Fe(II) by organic impurities so they eliminate the need for very pure water and materials.

See the instructor concerning the use of the irradiation source. Fill 3 weighing bottles with the Fe(II) solution, then stopper tightly. Irradiate the three samples for 1 minute, 3 minutes, and 5 minutes, respectively.

[2] Weiss, Allen, and Schwarz, *Proceedings of the International Conference on the Peaceful Uses of Atomic Energy*, Vol. 14, 179, New York: United Nations (1956).

Measure the Fe(III) concentration spectrophotometrically by means of a Beckman U.V. spectrophotometer. Measure the absorption at 304 millimicrons. Since a comparison method is used, it is not necessary to standardize the solution initially.

Data:

Calculate the radiation dose rate in rads using

$$R(r/hr) = \frac{10^9}{EbGt} (A_i - A_n)$$

where E = molar extinction coefficient (varies for each instrument but an average value is 2174 liters per mole-cm at 24°),

G = micromoles Fe(III) formed per liter per 1000r = 15.5 for this system,

b = sample thickness in cell,

t = irradiation time.

A_i and A_n are the optical densities for the irradiated sample and the non-irradiated sample. $A = \log (1/T)$ where T = transmittance.

EXPERIMENT 40

The Radiolysis of Methyl Iodide

Purpose:

To measure the amount of free iodine formed in the radiolysis of methyl iodide.

Method:

See the instructor concerning the use of the irradiation source. A 25 ml sample of pure, freshly distilled methyl iodide is irradiated for 10 minutes, after which time a 5 ml sample is withdrawn and the remaining 20 ml replaced in the irradiation source for an additional 10 minutes. After removal of another 5 ml sample, the remaining CH_3I is irradiated for another 20 minute interval. A third 5 ml sample is withdrawn and, after a final 40 minute irradiation, a fourth 5 ml sample. Thus, 5 ml samples of ten, twenty, forty, and eighty minutes irradiation time have been collected. As each sample is taken, it is pipetted into a 25 ml volumetric flask and diluted to the mark with dried *n*-hexane. (Keep the solutions in the dark as much as possible.)

Calibrate the spectrophotometer with solutions of I_2 in the range of 0.001 to 0.01 M in a solution of 20 ml *n*-hexane plus 5 ml CH_3I. The samples

for calibration and for analysis should be allowed to settle overnight to remove any turbidity before spectral measurement. Determine the absorption coefficient of each of the irradiated solutions with the spectrophotometer.

Data:

Use the calibration curve to determine the I_2 concentration of each irradiated sample and plot a curve for the concentration of I_2 as a function of irradiation time. Use this and the results of the previous experiment to calculate a $G(I_2)$ value.

REFERENCES

Barq, Z. M., and P. Alexander, *Fundamentals of Radio-biology*. London: Butterworth Scientific Publications, 1955.

Collinson, E., and A. J. Swallow, *Chem. Revs.*, **56**, 471 (1956).

Haissinsky, M., *La Chimie Nucléaire et ses Applications*. Paris: Masson et Cie, 1957.

Hamil, W. H., and R. R. Williams, *Principles of Physical Chemistry*. Englewood Cliffs, N. J.: Prentice-Hall, Inc., 1959, Chapter XVIII.

Harwood, Hausner, Morse, and Rauch, *Effects of Radiation on Materials*. New York: Reinhold Publishing Corp., 1958.

Lind Jubilee Symposium, *J. Chem. Educ.*, **36**, 262, 346 (1959).

Proceedings of the First International Conference on the Peaceful Uses of Atomic Energy (Geneva: United Nations), Vols. 7 and 14 (1956).

Proceedings of the Second International Conference on the Peaceful Uses of Atomic Energy (Geneva: United Nations), Vol. 29 (1959).

APPENDIX A

Special Projects

IN THE course upon which this book is based, the students have been encouraged to undertake special projects using radioactivity in their own fields of research interests. This is possible at Florida State University as the class is limited to graduate students and the enrollment is kept to a size (8 students) where close individual supervision is feasible. The student response to this plan has been excellent. After the first month or so of class, the students interested in a special project are required to submit a project proposal which states the proposed research and the purpose behind it, the experimental approach to be used (in some detail), the data to be obtained and the method of its interpretation. Usually the proposal fits into the thesis research of an advanced student, and the major professor is consulted before submission of the proposal. In other cases, the project has been suggested to the student by the instructor. Two to four weeks of laboratory time are allowed for these projects. Some judgment must be exercised by the instructor in deciding whether the project is feasible scientifically and can be done in a reasonable length of time. These special projects teach the student to think of radioactivity in his own research and, in the course at Florida State University, take the place of classwide organic and biochemical experiments in particular.

As indicative of the type of special project which is feasible, some titles of projects undertaken in the Florida State University course are listed below. Obviously, not all the proposals were successful, but all taught valuable lessons.

(1) In Vitro Studies of Fe^{59} Uptake by the Protein Components of Amphibian Blood.
(2) Study of the Rate of Exchange of 2,2-Diphenylcyclopropyl Phenyl Ketone with CH_3OH^3 under Basic Conditions.
(3) Effects of Thyroxine on Amino Acid Incorporation into Protein.
(4) Study of the Behavior of Ni^{63} and Rh^{102} on Anion Exchange Resin with Glycolic Acid as Eluant.
(5) Determination of the Potassium Content of Commercial Fertilizers by Measurement of Activity of K^{40} Present.

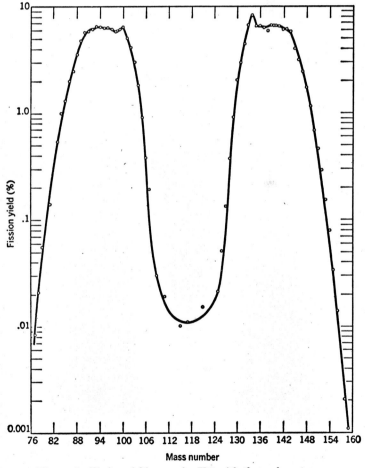

Figure 1. Fission yield curve for U^{235} with thermal neutrons.

For those students with inorganic and analytical majors who suggest no special project in particular, separation of fission products are substituted. Assignment of nuclides to be separated are made with a viewpoint to at-tempting to use the data to draw a total fission yield curve; i.e., to obtain a reasonable curve with relatively few nuclides if prior knowledge of the probable shape is used to reflect points. For example, if the fission was the result of slow neutron irradiation, then a curve similar to Figure 1 is to be expected. Thus, determination of the fission yield of Te^{127} and Te^{129} also gives reasonable values for A = 107 and A = 105, respectively.

Sr^{89}, Sr^{90}-Y^{90}, Y^{91}, Zr^{95}, $Ru^{103,106}$, Cd^{115m}, Sn^{123}, Sn^{125}-Sb^{125}, $Te^{127,129}$, I^{131}, Cs^{137}, Ba^{140}-La^{140}, $Ce^{141,144}$, Pr^{143}, Nd^{147}, $Eu^{155,156}$ are some nuclides of appropriate half lives and fission yields for use.

The student is given the task of selecting a separation procedure and counting technique. The experiment itself is a good exercise in the subject matter of this course as considerations of radiochemical purity, yield, decay factors and determination of absolute disintegration rates become very im-portant. It is necessary to have knowledge concerning the yields in the different mass number decay chain before a final answer can be calculated. The time which has elapsed between the fission and the isolation and measurement of a fission product must be known also.

A gross fission product mixture may be obtained from Oak Ridge, but the date of fission is then an uncertainty. However, even here where it may not be feasible to attempt evaluation of a fission yield curve, valuable experience is gained through measurement of the amount of a fission prod-uct nuclide in a complex mixture of radioactivities. Suitable separation schemes are obtainable from the following references:

Coryell, C. D., and N. Sugarman, *National Nuclear Energy Series*, IV, 9 (3 books). New York: McGraw-Hill Book Co., Inc., 1951.

Crouch, E. A. C., and G. B. Cook, *J. Inorg. Nucl. Chem.* 2, 223 (1956).

Finston, H. L., and J. Miskel, *Ann. Rev. Nuclear Sci.* 5, 169 (1955).

Garrison, W. M., and J. G. Hamilton, *Chemical Reviews* 49, 237 (1951).

Geiger, E. L., *Anal. Chem.* 31, 806 (1959).

Kleinberg, J., et al., *U. S. A. E. C. Los Alamos Report, LA-1721* (2nd rev.) (Washington, D. C.: Office of Technical Services, U. S. Dept. of Com-merce, 1958).

Meinke, W. W., *U. S. A. E. C. Reports AECD 2738, 2750,* and *3084* (Wash-ington, D. C.: Office of Technical Services, U. S. Dept. of Commerce).

Stevenson, P. C., and H. Hicks, *Ann. Rev. Nuclear Sci.* 3, 221 (1953).

Stewart, D. C., *Proceedings of the International Conference on the Peaceful Uses of Atomic Energy* (Geneva: United Nations); Paper 729, Vol. 7, 321 (1956).

Wilkinson, G., and W. E. Grummitt, *Nucleonics* 9, No. 3, 52 (1951).

Radiochemistry Monograph Series, NAS-NRC Nuclear Science Series (Washington, D. C.: Office of Technical Services, U. S. Dept. of Commerce).

For data on fission yield chains and fission yield curves, the following references may be consulted:

Katcoff, S., *Nucleonics*, 16, No. 4, 78 (1958).

Perkel, Leventhal, and Zumwalt, Chapter 8 in American Institute of Physics Handbook. New York: McGraw-Hill Book Co., Inc., 1957.

Steinberg, E. P., and L. E. Glendenin, *Proceedings of the International Conference on the Peaceful Uses of Atomic Energy* (Geneva: United Nations); Paper 614, Vol. 7, 3 (1956).

Blomeke, J. O., *U. S. A. E. C. Report, ORNL-1783*. (Washington, D. C.: Office of Technical Services, U. S. Dept. of Commerce.)

APPENDIX B

Licensing Regulations

Because of the special safety considerations involved in the use of radioisotopes, the U. S. Atomic Energy Commission has established certain controls over the use of reactor produced isotopes. There is no inherent danger present in the use of these not present in the use of cyclotron produced isotopes, but the former are much more easily produced in large quantities and are the activities offered for sale by Oak Ridge. The sale, possession, and use of such radioisotopes is governed by the rules and regulations formulated by the Commission and published in the Code of Federal Regulations, Title 10, Chapter 1, Parts 20 and 30. Anyone responsible for the use of radioisotopes should be familiar with these documents which may be obtained from

> United States Atomic Energy Commission
> Isotopes Branch
> Division of Licensing and Regulations
> 1717 H Street, N. W.
> Washington 25, D. C.

A general license has been granted whereby it is possible to obtain and possess a number of activities without prior AEC approval. Some activities and their generally licensed quantities are listed in Appendix C. Under the conditions of this general license, possession is limited to ten of these nuclides at any one time.

It is necessary to obtain a specific license for quantities in excess of those listed in Appendix C and for special nuclear materials such as the transuranic elements. Application for such a license is made through the Isotopes Division, U. S. A. E. C., Oak Ridge. The request for a specific license is considered from the viewpoint of proposed use, the radiological safety of the facilities wherein the activity will be used, and the qualifications of the applicant in relation to radiological safety. In addition to the conditions set forth in Title 10, Code of Federal Regulations, additional conditions may be included in the license. Title 10 requires a licensee to keep records of the receipt and disposal of all radioisotopes. Also, radiation records of all personnel and areas are required where the level of activity is above certain prescribed limits.

The method of disposal of radioisotopes frequently represents one of the more difficult aspects of the license request for which to gain approval. Title 10, Part 10 discusses disposal into the sanitary sewerage system of small amounts of activity. Larger amounts may be disposed of by burial in soil or at sea if permission is obtained. Also, it is possible to arrange shipment of the waste to Oak Ridge or other AEC facilities for disposal.

Sources of Isotopes

The United States Atomic Energy Commission initiated in 1946 the sale of reactor produced isotopes through the Oak Ridge National Laboratory. Since that time, ORNL has expanded this service to the point where over one hundred radioisotope preparations are offered for sale to authorized purchasers. Atomic Energy of Canada, Limited also offers a wide range of radioisotopes. In both of these cases, isotopes produced in nuclear reactors are supplied. Standard units of the activities may be purchased or arrangements may be made for a service irradiation to produce an isotope not standard or to obtain a higher level of specific activity. Catalogs of the isotopes for sale and the service facilities available may be obtained from

> Union Carbide Nuclear Company
> Oak Ridge National Laboratory
> Isotope Sales Department
> P. O. Box X
> Oak Ridge, Tennessee

and

> Atomic Energy of Canada, Limited
> Commercial Products Division
> P. O. Box 93
> Ottawa, Canada

For each isotope listed data is given on the specific activity, chemical form, and mode of production.

Some cyclotron produced activities are offered for sale by several industrial nuclear companies, such as Tracerlab, Inc. and Nuclear Science and Engineering Corp. Special service irradiations with cyclotrons may be arranged through Oak Ridge National Laboratory (protons) and the University of California, Lawrence Radiation Laboratory, Berkeley (protons, deuterons, and alphas). For the policy concerning use of other cyclotrons, the individual laboratories should be contacted.

Isotope Specialties Co., New England Nuclear Corp., Nuclear-Chicago Corp., Nucleonic Corp. of America, Tracerlab, and Volk Radiochemical Co. are only a few of the many concerns which sell radioisotopes and a large number of organic compounds in which carbon-14 or tritium has been incorporated. The annual Buyer's Guide Edition of the magazine *Nucleonics* is an excellent source of information about these labeled compounds.

The Oak Ridge National Laboratory distributes enriched stable isotopes. For the isotopes available and their degrees if enrichment, the Isotope Sales Division should be consulted.

APPENDIX C

A NUMBER of useful radioisotopes and the quantities of each which may be possessed under the general license granted by the AEC are listed below. The energies are the maximum beta energies; for both beta and gamma rays, only those in at least 5% abundance are given. One microcurie of any beta or gamma emitting isotope not included in this list falls under the exemption quantity of the general license. For a more complete listing of isotopes and their properties see the Table of Isotopes in *Reviews of Modern Physics*.[1]

Element	Isotope	Half life	E_β(Mev)	E_γ(Mev)	Quantity (microcuries)
Tritium	$_1H^3$	12.3 y	0.018 Mev	none	250
Berylium	$_4Be^7$	53.5 d	E. C.	0.478 X rays	50
Carbon	$_6C^{14}$	5568 y	0.155	none	50
Fluorine	$_9F^{18}$	112 min	0.64 (β^+)	none	50
Sodium	$_{11}Na^{22}$	2.6 y	0.54 (β^+)	1.28	10
	$_{11}Na^{24}$	15.0 h	1.40	1.37	10
				2.75	
Magnesium	$_{12}Mg^{28}$	21.2 h	0.42	0.032, 0.40,	1
				0.95, 1.35	
Phosphorus	$_{15}P^{32}$	14.3 d	1.71	none	10
Sulfur	$_{16}S^{35}$	87 d	0.168	none	50
Chlorine	$_{17}Cl^{36}$	3×10^5 y	0.71	none	1
Potassium	$_{19}K^{42}$	12.5 h	2.00	1.53	10
Calcium	$_{20}Ca^{45}$	164 d	0.255	none	10
Scandium	$_{21}Sc^{46}$	84 d	0.36	0.89, 1.12	1
Vanadium	$_{23}V^{48}$	16 d	0.694 (β^+)	0.986, 1.314	1
			E. C.	X rays	

[1] D. Strominger, J. M. Hollander, and G. T. Seaborg, *Revs. Modern Phys.* **30**, 585 (1958).

Element	Isotope	Half life	E_β(Mev)	E_γ(Mev)	Quantity (microcuries)
Chromium	$_{24}Cr^{51}$	27.8 d	E. C.	0.325 X rays	50
Manganese	$_{25}Mn^{52}$	5.7 d	$0.58(\beta^+)$	0.73, 0.94, 1.46	1
Iron	$_{26}Fe^{55}$	2.6 y	E. C.	none X rays	50
	$_{26}Fe^{59}$	45.1 d	0.27 0.46	1.098 1.289	1
Cobalt	$_{27}Co^{60}$	5.24 y	0.312	1.172, 1.332	1
Nickel	$_{28}Ni^{59}$	8×10^4 y	E. C.	none X rays	1
	$_{28}Ni^{63}$	125 y	0.067	none	1
Copper	$_{29}Cu^{64}$	12.8 h	$0.57(\beta^-)$ $0.65(\beta^+)$ E. C.	none X rays	50
Zinc	$_{30}Zn^{65}$	245 d	E. C.	1.119 X rays	10
Gallium	$_{31}Ga^{72}$	14.3 h	0.64 0.96 1.51 2.53 3.17	0.601, 0.630 0.834, 0.894 1.050, 1.595 1.859, 2.203 2.491, 2.508	10
Germanium	$_{32}Ge^{71}$	11.4 d	E. C.	none X rays	50
Arsenic	$_{33}As^{76}$	26.4 h	1.76 2.41 2.97	0.555 0.648 1.210	10
	$_{33}As^{77}$	38.7 h	0.68	none	10
Bromine	$_{35}Br^{82}$	35.9 h	0.444	0.554, 0.619, 0.698, 0.777 0.828, 1.044 1.317, 1.475	1
Rubidium	$_{37}Rb^{86}$	18.7 d	0.71, 1.78	1.08	10
Strontium	$_{38}Sr^{89}$	50.5 d	1.46	none	1
	$_{38}Sr^{90}$	27.7 y	0.545 (Also Y^{90} radiations if present)	none	0.1
Yttrium	$_{39}Y^{90}$	64.2 h	2.26	none	1
	$_{39}Y^{91}$	57.5 d	1.54	none	1
Zirconium	$_{40}Zr^{95}$	65 d	0.360 0.396	0.722 0.754	1
Niobium	$_{41}Nb^{95}$	35 d	0.158	0.765	10
Molybdenum	$_{42}Mo^{99}$	66.0 h	0.41 1.18	0.140, 0.745, 0.780, 0.850	10
Technetium	$_{43}Tc^{96}$	4.20 d	E. C.	0.771, 0.806, 0.842, 1.119 X rays	1
	$_{43}Tc^{99}$	2.1×10^5 y	0.29	none	1
Ruthenium	$_{44}Ru^{106}$	1.00 y	0.039	none (Also Rh^{106} radiations)	1
Rhodium	$_{45}Rh^{103m}$	57 min	I. T.	0.040	(See Pd^{103})
	$_{45}Rh^{105}$	36.5 h	0.25, 0.56	0.32	10
	$_{45}Rh^{106}$	30 sec	2.44, 3.1, 3.53	0.513, 0.624, 1.045	(See Ru^{106})
Palladium	$_{46}Pd^{103}$	17.0 d	E. C.	0.040 (Rh^{103m}) 0.298, 0.362, 0.498 X rays	50
	$_{46}Pd^{109}$	13.5 h	1.03	0.087 (from 40 sec Ag^{109m} daughter)	10
Silver	$_{47}Ag^{105}$	40 d	E. C.	0.064, 0.281, 0.345, 0.443, 0.654 X rays	1

Element	Isotope	Half life	E_β(Mev)	E_γ(Mev)	Quantity (microcuries)
Silver	$_{47}Ag^{110m}$	253 d	0.087, 0.530	0.446, 0.657, 0.677, 0.705, 0.764, 0.817, 0.884, 0.937, 1.384, 1.504	1
	$_{47}Ag^{111}$	7.6 d	0.70, 1.04	0.243, 0.340	10
Cadmium	$_{47}Cd^{109}$	470 d	E. C.	0.087 X rays	10
Indium	$_{49}In^{114m}$	50 d	I. T.	0.190	1
	$_{49}In^{114}$	72 sec	1.984	none	
Tin	$_{50}Sn^{113}$	119 d	E. C.	0.260, 0.393	10
Antimony	$_{51}Sb^{124}$	60.9 d	0.24, 0.61, 0.97, 1.60, 2.32	0.603, 0.646, 0.723, 1.692	1
	$_{51}Sb^{125}$	2.0 y	0.128 0.299 0.444 0.616	0.175, 0.43, 0.46, 0.60, 0.64	1
Tellurium	$_{52}Te^{127m}$	105 d	I. T.	0.089	10
	$_{52}Te^{127}$	9.4 h	0.70	none	
Iodine	$_{53}I^{131}$	8.08 d	0.335 0.608	0.284 0.364 0.637	10
Cesium	$_{55}Cs^{134}$	2.07 y	0.083 0.655 0.683	0.565, 0.570, 0.606, 0.797, 0.802	1
	$_{55}Cs^{137}$	26.6 y	0.51, 1.17	0.662	1
Barium	$_{56}Ba^{140}$	12.8 d	0.48, 1.02	0.030, 0.537 (See La^{140})	1
Lanthanum	$_{57}La^{140}$	40.2 h	0.42, 0.86, 1.15, 1.36, 1.62, 2.20	0.328, 0.438, 0.490, 0.815, 1.60	10
Cerium	$_{58}Ce^{141}$	33.1 d	0.442, 0.581	0.142	1
	$_{58}Ce^{144}$	285 d	0.175, 0.309	0.033, 0.042, 0.054, 0.081, 0.133 (Also Pr^{144} radiations)	1
Praseodymium	$_{59}Pr^{143}$	13.7 d	0.932	none	10
	$_{59}Pr^{144}$	17.3 min	2.98	none	(See Ce^{144})
Promethium	$_{61}Pm^{147}$	2.64 y	0.223	none	10
Samarium	$_{62}Sm^{153}$	47.1 h	0.26, 0.69, 0.80	0.65, 0.72, 0.83	10
Europium	$_{63}Eu^{154}$	16 y	0.12, 0.25, 0.55, 0.83, 1.84	0.123, 0.725, 0.875, 0.998, 1.007, 1.227	1
	$_{63}Eu^{155}$	1.7 y	0.154, 0.243	0.0188, 0.0865, 0.1052	1
Thulium	$_{69}Tm^{170}$	129 d	0.884, 0.968	0.084	1
Hafnium	$_{72}Hf^{181}$	44.6 d	0.408	0.004, 0.133, 0.482	1
Tantalum	$_{73}Ta^{182}$	115 d	0.36, 0.44, 0.514	0.068, 0.100, 0.156, 0.179, 0.222, 0.229, 0.264, 1.122, 1.189, 1.222, 1.231	10
Tungsten	$_{74}W^{185}$	75.8 d	0.430	none	10
Rhenium	$_{75}Re^{186}$	88.9 h	0.934, 1.072	0.137	10
Iridium	$_{77}Ir^{192}$	74.4 d	0.67	0.296, 0.309, 0.3165, 0.468, 0.588, 0.605, 0.613	10
Gold	$_{79}Au^{198}$	2.70 d	0.290	0.412	10
	$_{79}Au^{199}$	3.14 d	0.251, 0.302, 0.460	0.050, 0.158, 0.208	10
Mercury	$_{80}Hg^{203}$	46.9 d	0.208	0.279	1
Thallium	$_{81}Tl^{204}$	3.56 y	0.764	none	50
Polonium	$_{84}Po^{210}$	138.4 d	5.31 (α)	0.804	0.1

APPENDIX D

Counting Equipment for the Course

AN IDEAL counting laboratory for a course based on this text would include facilities for Geiger, proportional and scintillation counting. In addition, a single channel gamma spectrometer and a linear or a logarithmic count-rate meter would be available. However, it may not be possible to obtain all this equipment at first. A very basic counting arrangement would include a scaler, a high voltage power supply and a Geiger-Müller detector. All but the following experiments can be performed with only this basic Geiger counting equipment: 1, 3, 13, 14, and 15. For Experiments 16, 17, 18, 19, and 20 it is necessary to have a source of neutrons in addition. Experiments 39 and 40 require a relatively high radiation source.

The next addition should be a scintillation counter. If an appropriate scaler is chosen for the Geiger-Müller counting arrangement, the same scalar and high-voltage power supply may be used with a scintillation probe. Interchangeable anthracene, zinc sulfide, and sodium iodide crystals should be obtained with the scintillation probe for beta, alpha, and gamma counting. A proportional counter is especially valuable for counting alpha and low-energy beta emitters as well as for determination of high count rates.

It is impossible to attempt an evaluation of even a significant part of the counting equipment offered by the numerous manufacturers in this field. Nuclear-Chicago Corporation offers a basic Geiger-Müller counting arrangement for educational use. It includes their Model 151A decade scaler, D-34 detector, M-2A sample mount, and T-101 interval timer. Baird-Atomic also includes several such basic counting groups. At Florida State University, we have used Hamner Electronics decade scalers Model N-230. These are used with Geiger-Müller detectors, with Model DR-15 proportional counters of the Nuclear Corp. of America and with DS-5 scintillation detectors from Nuclear-Chicago. The latter are housed in the Nuclear-Chicago Model 3054 lead shield. Some analogous scalers are Nuclear-Chicago Model 186, Tracerlab Versamatic SC-73, and Nucleonic Corp. of America RCR-2, to mention only a very few. The Hamner single channel Manual Spectrometer N-1261M is quite satisfactory, as well as the Hamner N-701B logarithmic count rate meter and the Nuclear-Chicago 1619A and the 1620B linear rate meter. A Varian Recorder Model G-10 has been very useful in measuring short half lives and in scanning chromatograms. For these experiments it records the output of a count rate meter which receives the signal from a Geiger-Müller tube. The annual Buyer's Guide Edition of the magazine *Nucleonics* is an excellent reference source on counting equipment and its suppliers.

Nucleonics Corp. of America, Tracerlab, Nuclear-Chicago Corp., and Radiation Counter Laboratories are a few of the many concerns which supply the accessories for a radiochemical laboratory. Lead bricks, counting planchets, sets of aluminum and lead absorbers, and micropipets are only a few of these accessories. A Heath Co. battery eliminator Model BE-5 is a good laboratory power supply for the electroplating experiments. Pocket dosimeters and survey meters are also obtainable from many firms, including those listed above. Inexpensive survey meters are available which operate on flashlight batteries and are adequate for the purposes of this course.

APPENDIX E

Terms and Definitions

Isotopes: Nuclear species which have the same atomic number (Z) but different mass numbers (A). Thus, Na^{22}, Na^{23}, and Na^{24} are all isotopes of sodium; Na^{22} and Na^{24} are radioactive isotopes of sodium, whereas Na^{23} is stable.

Nuclide: A general term indicating any nuclear species with specific Z and A. Both Na^{22} and C^{14} are nuclides but are not isotopic to each other.

Proton: The nucleus of a hydrogen atom; $Z = 1$, $A = 1$.

Neutron: A nuclear particle; $Z = 0$, $A = 1$.

Deuteron: The nucleus of an isotope of hydrogen with $A = 2$. This nucleus contains one proton and one neutron.

Nucleon: A general term for the constituent particles of a nucleus. Thus, Na^{23} (an isotope of sodium, whose atomic number is 11) has 23 nucleons, i.e., 11 protons and 12 neutrons.

Alpha particle: The nucleus of a helium atom, i.e., $Z = 2$, $A = 4$.

Beta particle: The particle emitted by a nucleus when a radioactive nucleus changes Z by one unit, with no change in A. It is identical with an electron of either positive or negative charge.

Negatron: A negative beta particle. A negatron is emitted when there is an increase of Z by one; e.g., $_{11}Na^{24} \rightarrow {}_{12}Mg^{24} + \beta^-$.

215

Positron: A positive beta particle. In positron emission, there is a decrease in Z; e.g.,

$$_{11}\text{Na}^{22} \longrightarrow {}_{10}\text{Ne}^{22} + \beta^+$$

Electron capture: An alternative process to positron emission, where a nucleus emits no particles but decreases in Z by one unit by capturing an orbital electron, most frequently from the K shell; e g.,

$$_{56}\text{Ba}^{133} \xrightarrow{\text{E.C.}} {}_{55}\text{Cs}^{133}$$

Gamma rays: Nuclear emissions, where $Z = 0$ and $A = 0$. These are electromagnetic radiations usually found accompanying alpha or beta decay of a nucleus. They are the nuclear counterparts of atomic X rays.

Isomeric transition: The process whereby a nuclide in a metastable nuclear state passes to a nuclear state of lower energy, with emission of a gamma ray; e.g.,

$$_{79}\text{Au}^{197m} \xrightarrow{\text{I.T.}} {}_{79}\text{Au}^{197} + \gamma$$

Half life: The characteristic value of the length of time for a particular radioactive species to decay to one-half of its initial level of activity.

Fission: The nuclear process whereby a heavy nucleus breaks into two large fragments, emitting simultaneously one or more neutrons and a large amount of energy.

Electron-volt: The amount of energy acquired by an electron when it is accelerated by an electric potential of 1 volt. Nuclear energies are usually expressed in kev (thousand electron volts) or Mev (million electron volts).

$$1 \text{ Mev} = 1.602 \times 10^{-6} \text{ erg} = 3.827 \times 10^{-14} \text{ calorie}$$

Carrier-free: A term denoting the absence of any non-radioactive isotopes. Thus, Na^{22} will be carrier-free if it has no inactive Na^{23} associated with it.

Curie: A unit of radioactivity defined as that quantity of any radioactive nuclide where the number of disintegrations per second is 3.700×10^{10}, or 2.22×10^{12} disintegrations per minute. The millicurie (10^{-3} curie) and microcurie (10^{-6} curie) are also units in common use.

TABLE OF CONSTANTS

Velocity of light	c	$= 2.99776 \times 10^{10}$ cm sec^{-1}
Faraday constant	F	$= 96500$ abs coul 1g equiv.
Electronic charge	e	$= 4.8025 \times 10^{-10}$ abs esu
		$= 1.60203 \times 10^{-19}$ abs coulombs
Planck constant	h	$= 6.624 \times 10^{-27}$ erg sec
Avogadro's number	N	$= 6.0228 \times 10^{23}$ mole^{-1}
Mass of electron	m	$= 9.1066 \times 10^{-28}$ gm
Atomic weight of electron. .	m	$= 5.4862 \times 10^{-4}$ (physical scale)
Mass of unit atomic weight .	M_0	$= 1.66035 \times 10^{-24}$ gm
Nuclear radius.	R	$= 1.4 \times 10^{-13} A^{1/3}$ (A = mass number)

Atomic weights:

Hydrogen	M_H	$= 1.00814$
Helium	M_{He}	$= 4.00387$
Neutron	M_n	$= 1.00899$

Energy equivalence . . . . 1 atomic mass unit = 931 Mev
$$= 1.49 \times 10^{-3} \text{ erg}$$
$$= 3.56 \times 10^{-11} \text{ cal}$$

1 electron mass = 0.510 Mev

1 Mev $= 1.07 \times 10^{-3}$ amu
$$= 1.60 \times 10^{-6} \text{ erg}$$
$$= 3.82 \times 10^{-14} \text{ cal}$$

1 ev/molecule = 23.06 kcal/mole

Time:

Number seconds in a day .	8.64×10^4
Number seconds in a year.	3.1536×10^7
Number minutes in a day.	1440
Number minutes in a year.	5.2596×10^5
Number hours in a year .	8.766×10^3

1 H 1.0080																	2 He 4.003
3 Li 6.940	4 Be 9.013											5 B 10.82	6 C 12.010	7 N 14.008	8 O 16.000	9 F 19.00	10 Ne 20.183
11 Na 22.997	12 Mg 24.32											13 Al 26.98	14 Si 28.09	15 P 30.975	16 S 32.066	17 Cl 35.457	18 A 39.944
19 K 39.100	20 Ca 40.08	21 Sc 44.96	22 Ti 47.90	23 V 50.95	24 Cr 52.01	25 Mn 54.93	26 Fe 55.85	27 Co 58.94	28 Ni 58.69	29 Cu 63.54	30 Zn 65.38	31 Ga 69.72	32 Ge 72.60	33 As 74.91	34 Se 78.96	35 Br 79.916	36 Kr 83.80
37 Rb 85.48	38 Sr 87.63	39 Y 88.92	40 Zr 91.22	41 Nb 92.91	42 Mo 95.95	43 Tc	44 Ru 101.7	45 Rh 102.91	46 Pd 106.7	47 Ag 107.880	48 Cd 112.41	49 In 114.76	50 Sn 118.70	51 Sb 121.76	52 Te 127.61	53 I 126.91	54 Xe 131.3
55 Cs 132.91	56 Ba 137.36	57 La SEE La SERIES	72 Hf 178.6	73 Ta 180.88	74 W 183.92	75 Re 186.31	76 Os 190.2	77 Ir 193.1	78 Pt 195.23	79 Au 197.2	80 Hg 200.61	81 Tl 204.39	82 Pb 207.21	83 Bi 209.00	84 Po	85 At	86 Rn
87 Fr	88 Ra	89 Ac SEE Ac SERIES	(104)	(105)	(106)	(107)	(108)										

LANTHANIDE SERIES

57 La 138.92	58 Ce 140.13	59 Pr 140.92	60 Nd 144.27	61 Pm	62 Sm 150.43	63 Eu 152.0	64 Gd 156.9	65 Tb 159.2	66 Dy 162.46	67 Ho 164.94	68 Er 167.2	69 Tm 169.4	70 Yb 173.04	71 Lu 174.99

ACTINIDE SERIES

89 Ac	90 Th 232.12	91 Pa 231	92 U 238.07	93 Np 237	94 Pu 239	95 Am 243	96 Cm 244	97 Bk 249	98 Cf 252	99 E 253	100 Fm 254	101 Mv 256	102 254	(103)

Index